In God We Trust

A Legacy For Creating Wealth And Abundance

Jon D. Bender

First published by AuthorHouse 11/20/05

ISBN: 1-4208-9367-X (sc)
ISBN: 1-4208-9366-1 (dj)

Library of Congress Control Number: 2005909873

Printed in the United States of America
Bloomington, Indiana

This book is printed on acid-free paper.

Dedication

To my Lord and Savior Jesus Christ,

my beautiful wife Sherie
and my two wonderful sons
Nicholas and Alex

Acknowledgements

I would like to say thank you to: Greg Montoya and Michael J. Jackson, Sr. for believing in and supporting me over the last decade; Mitchell Tolle for his artful God-centered inspiration; · Shary Jones, Paul Svetz, Gary Hassell, Bill Davis, Robert Brickman, Dr. James Miller and Vic Conant for their kind encouragement; Dr. David Kendall, Leslie Blackwell, Cindy Quick and Scot Frenzel for their editorial suggestions and proofing; Jack Small and Elaine Gibson for their endorsement assistance; lastly, my Mom and Dad who gave me my first exposure to love and encouragement.

Foreword

When I was 16 years old my dad handed me a book that changed my life. It started me on my lifelong pursuit of personal growth. This book was the classic, How To Win Friends And Influence People by Dale Carnegie. What I learned in this book literally hit me between the eyes. It convicted me. It illuminated much insecurity and explained why I didn't have that many friends. However in this realization, it also helped me create many good questions related to what I was going to do about it and how I was going to enjoy the process. Over the next 5 years I developed a passion for growth and studied virtually every thing I could get my hands on related to personal growth studies. I devoured works by Ziglar, Nightingale, Rohn, Tracy, Mandino, Covey, Robbins, Hill, Carnegie, Wattles and Peale to name only a few. As I grew, I began to look at the world much differently. I started to look at the world as a chronic good-finder and focused on what was possible. I began to believe that with practice and by setting up new rules regarding what defined success that I virtually could not fail at anything.

I took this new found personal growth and confidence into the entrepreneurial world after graduating from college in electrical engineering only to find that my youthful idealism was quickly checked by the realities of life. During this time my dreams were dashed not once, but twice with the companies I began either going out of business or going bankrupt. After two rounds of unemployment lines and driving an $800 car, my personal growth and confidence began to collapse. I felt as though I somehow had miscalculated my value and sense of destiny.

Daily readings and study in personal growth slowly returned my belief that maybe I had just gone through a season of testing so I once again began to explore entrepreneurial endeavors. I was amazed when I stumbled across an opportunity to put many of my years of personal growth study into leading and supporting others. I quickly excelled in this opportunity and began making more money than I had ever made in my life, but that wasn't enough. I so desperately wanted to be important and significant so I subconsciously set off to prove my importance and significance with awards, recognition and accolades. When I reached the top of a multi-hundred million dollar company in the area of sales, I found that I had arrived, but where I had arrived wasn't what I thought it would be. For the next several years, although financially comfortable in lifestyle, I was insecure and uncomfortable with me. There was still something missing.

And then it happened. On November 13, 1998, I became a Christian. The "Jesus thing" absolutely turned my life upside down. Up to that point in my life all that I had done had been about pleasing me, making me significant, having me recognized and having me be important. My new life as a Christian quickly changed all that. It was no longer all about me. This was a very confusing time in my life as I had been conditioned for decades by my insecurity for survival by making sure I got my due, but then something wonderful happened. God changed my heart. I stopped focusing on what I could get and began focusing on what I could give. What may be interesting to the entrepreneurial reader is that with this transition in my personal growth came a huge transition in my wealth not just financial wealth, but true wealth which affects all facets of life. When I stopped focusing on how much money I could make and started focusing on how many people I could serve, the money came pouring in.

Today, millions of dollars later, I am so grateful not just for the freedom, but more importantly for whom God has helped me become in the process. I have the pleasure and honor in leading thousands of people in entrepreneurial endeavors and have the honor to contribute positively to many people's quality of life. I don't say this to impress you, but rather to impress upon you I am the guy that stood in the unemployment line not once, but twice and who drove an $800 car. I am the guy who overcompensated for my insecurity by winning recognition at all costs. I am the guy who was destroyed and then restored. I am just a guy who finally discovered how to be grateful.

I am honored to somehow share with you some of the many lessons I have learned about wealth and gratitude in this modern fable. I am humbled that I could be used to share this proven and guaranteed path to wealth with you. As you read these pages, I ask that God's bountiful blessing be upon you. I ask that He expands your capacity for prosperity and joy as you read. I ask that He favor you and has His hand on every aspect of your life and I finally ask that He protect you from any misunderstanding or deception as you reflect and apply to your life anything that you might take away from this work. Thank you for the honor and privilege to share with you.

Prologue

An open letter to any serious person desiring wealth

How To Use This Book To Become Wealthy...Guaranteed!

Have you ever wondered why some people are so much wealthier than others? This is a question that I have myself asked for years. What I have discovered is that true wealth doesn't just happen; you have to make it happen. Every person who has ever made it to the top (and stayed there) didn't get there by accident; they got there by being persistent, and whether they know it or not have been following certain time-tested principles and laws that guarantee success. The amazing thing is that all of these principles and laws are timeless, yet most people live their lives without ever discovering them and end up believing that success is only for a fortunate few!

Learning to Become Wealthy The Easy Way

Jon Bender's book, <u>*In God We Trust*</u>, is an American classic with a legacy teaching that reveals three laws necessary to achieve true wealth. It is an inspiring, easy to read, heart wrenching story that hits home for any person who desires to be wealthy. Jon walks you through the ails of our society that hold people back from success and at the same time reveals the most powerful cure to overcome these obstacles: trust in God and the virtues that emanate from it. People from all beliefs and from all walks of life can become wealthy from reading this book. Every chapter shares profound wisdom, strategy, insight, and optimism articulated by one most prominent, inspired leaders of our day.

This remarkable work uses a unique story-type approach for teaching the most important laws of wealth and how to apply them systematically to both business as well as your personal life. It does so in a progressive blueprint manner that captures the reader's attention and compels them to want to keep reading. This story is fictional yet it has a real life feel that builds confidence in knowing that wealth *is* within reach of *all* who persistently seek and understand it.

As an entrepreneur, I have been in business for many years and by the Grace of God have made millions of dollars. You may have heard it said "If I knew back then what I know now, imagine how much more successful I would be today." Fortunately, you are now reading a guide that reveals wealth truths that most self-made millionaires have had to discover by trail-and-error and through pain-and-suffering. You are only moments a way from beginning a journey that can give you a distinct advantage over many other people who search only for riches.

Maximize Your Benefits And Succeed Even Faster

To get the most out of this book go to an inspiring location that will allow you to visualize what it would feel like to live a life of abundance. Go and sit in the lobby area of the fanciest hotel that you can find. Or go to an upscale resort and overlook the mountains, the ocean or golf course. The combined effect of reading this book and doing so in an affluent type environment could positively change your life in ways that you may have never imagined possible, I guarantee it!

Keep in mind that money is not a true measurement of wealth. The ability to live in a constant state of gratitude is! Even though I am grateful for all the abundance God has provided for my family, I am confident that if I had read this book when I first started in business my life would be 10 times more abundant today.

If you have ever wanted to take the mystery out of why some people are so much wealthier than others, take the time to carefully read and study this book. Read it again and again. I sincerely believe it will open up your eyes, give you peripheral vision and allow you to see unlimited opportunities all around you that you never knew existed. I believe it will give you great confidence in knowing that wealth *is* within your reach, YES WEALTH IS FOR YOU TOO!

Greg Montoya

God Made Millionaire

CONTENTS

1

Whose Child Are You?

A cold, biting mist began to evaporate as the sun poked its face over Warrior Mountain. With purpose and direction, the brilliant light slowly released the pines and maples from the grips of darkness, revealing a glistening white spring frost. Tucked in the side of the mountain, a tiny rough-hewn timber cabin sat quietly above the small town of Saluda, North Carolina. Along one side of the cabin, ice-covered bushes sparkled as frosty tree-tops shimmered and slowly emerged into the new day's light.

Six-year-old Jim Smith woke up, rubbed the sleep from his chestnut brown eyes and climbed off his rickety antique bed. A cowlick on the right side of his forehead left spikes of his brown hair shooting out in all directions. His tiny feet felt the cold as he quietly

1

creaked across the old wooden floor. He did not want to wake his sleeping mother. He made his way across one of only two rooms in the cabin. It was cold, very cold. With each breath, a frosty cloud of condensation left his small opened mouth. He grabbed a yellowing old paper from underneath the empty kindling bin beside the century old iron stove and was about to rip the paper in half when he noticed the date printed across the top. He carefully focused on the February 23, 1940. That was his birthday. Only a few weeks earlier, he and his mother had celebrated his turning six years old. But with deliberate and practiced movements, he returned to his task at hand, folding the torn newspaper over and again until it was the exact width needed to fit in the bottom of his shoes. He carefully slid folded paper into the bottom of each shoe to keep the outdoor frigid air and frozen dew from creeping in through the cracks in the soles. Then he reached for his tattered old woolen coat. It only had one of its four buttons left. He pulled it snug around his small body and headed outside for firewood.

As Jim gathered kindling for the stove, the warmth of each hand left a hand-print in the white covering of frost that had settled on the dry wood. With each added piece, he felt the frosty bite of frozen wetness grow. His small fingers grew numb. He tried not to think about the cold but instead about how quickly the dry wood would get the fire going and how good breakfast would be. He knew in no time at all the familiar smell of country ham and sound of frying eggs would fill the cabin. Even though his mother had been sick lately she always managed to make breakfast time warm and the meals filling. At age six, Jim already knew that, like it or not, he was the man of the family.

Jim and his mother struggled daily. Susan Smith, a single mother, had done the best she knew how to provide for her son. As poor as they were, she always kept a positive outlook in spite of her frequent bouts with walking pneumonia. She worked three jobs just to make ends meet and sometimes arrived home to find Jim had already fallen asleep on the bed. Their house was a drafty hand-me-down given to Susan when her great-great grandmother died. It was wet in the spring, hot in the summer and downright cold in the winter. The rusted wood-burning stove often filled the house with black smoke from a partially blocked chimney which irritated Susan's persistent cough. An icebox with dents and rusted hinges kept food from spoiling most of the time. Still his mother seemed to find bits of time here and there to sew or craft things like quilts, window curtains, and candles that allowed their home to feel cozy and safe.

Jim never knew his father. The kids in Saluda would often pick on him by calling him names like "bastard boy." The meanest kids would joke that his mother didn't know who his father was. Jim was a teenager before he learned about World War II and began to understand why they claimed she used to swim after the troop ships. The relentless teasing made Jim's stomach ball up in knots. He wanted to hide every time he came in contact with kids his own age, but Saluda was small and there was nowhere to hide. By the time they finished with their teasing, he had come to believe he had a disease – a disease that everyone knew about, but no one could cure.

His mother was treated no better. A single mother and a working woman, she was an outcast by any reckoning thought the town folk knew she had no money and that every penny she made went to provide for her son. Even so, every time she went to town to get groceries, women would whisper and laugh as she walked by. Despite the cruel gossip, Susan stayed strong, held her head high, and moved with dignified grace and kindness as she passed by the town's people.

Saluda had just over seven hundred people, so wherever Jim went, there were people who shunned and judged him as a "poor little bastard" that lived on the hill. Most of the parents in town would not allow their children to talk or play with him and acted as if they thought their own child would catch the same disease Jim imagined he had. When on rare occasions a child tried to say hello or play with him, they were promptly scolded and jerked away. Those things that Jim didn't understand as a young boy, he quickly came to realize in the following years. His life with his mother was difficult. They had few options, no money to relocate, and had to make the best of it.

In the first grade, Jim was a bright and dedicated student. His classmates were not interested in his grades; instead they acted out their parents' behavior with cruelty only children can know. His teacher seemed to care and scolded the guilty children, declaring that if they didn't stop they would not be allowed on the playground when time came for recess or worse. Still the kids were relentless with their taunts. So during recess, Jim often stayed inside where it seemed safest. He came to this realization after his fifth time of being sent home with a black eye or bloody nose. He had no friends, he trusted no one, and felt completely alone.

During class one day, Jim pulled out a prized possession from his pocket and flipped it over and over with his little fingers. He looked at the shiny silver dollar and thought about the hours he had spent stacking wood and doing odds jobs at Mrs. Jacob's. The old woman, concerned about Susan, had begun early on looking out for Jim by giving him yard chores and other various jobs where he could earn a dollar here and there. He studied the heavy coin in his hands and let his mind wander for a minute. He tried to imagine what rich was like, what it might be like to have a million of these when he could barely count to one hundred. He studied the coin's beautiful embossed design and carefully and read the words that he knew. He looked at the beautiful profile of Miss Liberty on the front of the coin and the perched eagle on the back. As his mind wandered, something very special happened. It literally jumped out at him.

On the front of the coin, to the left of Miss Liberty, "IN GOD WE," and to her right the word, "TRVST," an art deco form of the word TRUST. Jim tried to make sense out of the words, and though his mother had sometimes read to him from the Bible, he still wondered quietly exactly who was God? Then he thought to himself that surely God wouldn't like him. Why would He? No one else did. God couldn't possibly care for a boy like me, he thought. But he continued to stare at the words, "IN GOD WE TRUST." The four words seemed to beckon him while he wondered if there really was a God, where would he find this God.

Jim had heard some of the town's folks call the church, "God's house." Maybe he could find God there. He knew there was a

6

new pastor at the church in town but he had never been to church before. What was it like, he thought, and how could he go without letting anybody know? He decided that he could sneak in to see God without God seeing him. He knew his mother would be working on the ironing that she took in each week and wouldn't notice him gone for a little while. His six-year-old reasoning told him it was worth a try.

That Sunday Jim decided to go to church. The church was an old country church that stood near the center of town for more than a century. Its rock foundation gave way to a wood structure coated with peeling white paint. The one-room sanctuary was brightly lit with marbled stained-glass windows. Jim waited until the church service had started. He opened and closed the church door silently. He tip-toed around the back corner of the sanctuary, quietly slipped into the last pew where no one was sitting, and slouched down, watching and waiting to get a glimpse of God. He didn't know why he felt safe here. In fact, many of the people that picked on him were just a few pews away. Jim was filled with delight as he listened to the beautiful singing, and the new pastor sure could talk fancy. Jim peeked over the pew several times during the service hoping to see God. He figured maybe God was sitting up front so he often strained his neck up to peek over the old wooden scroll-backed pew in hopes of catching a glimpse. Not wanting to be seen, he leaned back on the threadbare red velvet pew cushions and looked at the church ceiling. He listened to the pastor's sermon, trying to understand what he could. As soon as the pastor stopped talking and sat down, Jim quietly slipped out the back door.

For the next few weeks, Jim slipped in and out of the church service without anyone knowing, or so he thought. However, the young pastor had seen the child sneaking in and out of church service, had curiously watched the mysterious bobbing of this little boy's head as he peeked from behind the pew.

The following Sunday, Jim slipped into the back pew as usual. But this time he stayed until after the last song. As he started to dart out, just before the end of the benediction, he heard a loud voice.

"You there, young man!" the pastor called from the pulpit.

Everyone gasped and turned to see who the pastor had called to. Jim slowly turned around. He could feel his heart racing and his shoulders tense up. Maybe this was a dream. No-a nightmare! He wanted to run, but his legs were paralyzed with fear. The congregation buzzed in a hushed whisper as the pastor stepped down from the pulpit and started walking toward him. The congregation seemed to be frozen in silence. The pastor walked up to Jim and leaned over to speak.

"I have seen you sneaking in and out of here for weeks," he said. "Whose boy are you?"

The congregation remained dead silent. Jim was so terrified he couldn't speak and he didn't dare look up. The pastor knelt down and cupped the boy's small face with his warm hand. Gently, he lifted Jim's chin.

"Well, now, hold on a minute," the pastor smiled and said in a loud, loving voice for all to hear. "I know whose boy you are. The resemblance is absolutely unmistakable." He put his other strong compassionate hand on Jim's bony little shoulder and said loudly, "You are a child of God! And son, that's a powerful family name you got there, boy. You better see that you live up to it!"

Jim's tiny brown, tear-filled eyes rose to meet the pastor's who continued to give him a warm smile as his hand slid down to gently grasp his arm. The corners of Jim's mouth slowly turned up in relief before breaking into a shy smile. With that the young pastor winked, and Jim, without hesitation, darted out of the church.

If God Is For You, Who Can Be Against You?

"Whether a job's big or small, do it right or not at all;

Once a job has begun, see it through until it's done."

Nancy Hanks, Abraham Lincoln's mother

For the next 10 years, life for Jim and his mother was still difficult. Although they struggled financially and his mother's health had worsened, something was different. The young pastor had since moved away to start another church, while still in Saluda he had shown much kindness to Jim and his mother and had patiently taught Jim about God and His word in the Bible. Jim didn't really care anymore what people in the town said about him or his mother because he had come to believe in himself and was confident that God loved him and had a plan for him. He may have been penniless, but he wasn't poor. Jim figured God had made no mistakes, not even when he created Jim. Hardly a day passed that Jim didn't think about what the young pastor had said to him on that special Sunday years ago.

Jim was 16 now, with a part-time job after school at Mrs. Thompson's grocery store. The store also had a post office. In the morning, Mrs. Thompson would let Jim deliver the Saluda newspaper to make extra money. Jim was a hard worker, a quick learner, and so honest and dependable that Mrs. Thompson had begun letting him close the store at the end of the workday.

A self-taught business owner, Mrs. Thompson had stressed the importance of making a profit. By way of examples, she explained things in simple and sensible ways like using a case of green beans to teach the difference between income and profit. She explained that in a case of green beans the revenue from ten of the twelve cans covered the cost of case, but that only the revenue generated from the remaining two cans was the profit that could be used for expenses and wages. Thus, Jim developed an early appreciation for the difference between profit and break-even.

Mrs. Thompson was a charitable woman. She taught Jim about the importance of doing something well and finishing the job. There wasn't a day that went by that Jim didn't hear her say in a sing-song rhyme, "Whether a job's big or small, do it right or not at all, and once a job has begun, see it through until it's done."

Each morning before school, Jim picked up a bundle of newspapers from the front of Thompson's store, loaded up his bag with papers, and began to pedal his bike through the streets of Saluda. He wondered why some people seemed to have so much money while others seem not to have any. What did the rich do? How did they get their money? He had overheard customers at the store say that money was the root of all evil, but how could something as useful as money really be evil?

As Jim glided by the houses delivering papers, he accidentally tossed one against a huge oak tree in the Johnson's yard. As he stopped to retrieve the paper, he noticed the headline, "New York Billionaire Moves to Asheville Amidst Accusations, Donates Three Million Dollars to Local Orphanage." He read the headline again, this time focusing on four words, "Billionaire" and "Donates Three Million." Slowly and methodically, he straddled his bike while trying to comprehend the idea of those four words. This time he pedaled slowly and wondered what it was like to be a billionaire. And how much is a billion, anyway, he thought, how could someone have so much money that they could give away three million dollars?

Jim shook his head and shrugged his shoulders. He knew that a million was less than a billion, but both amounts were beyond his comprehension.

Jim continued to weave his way through his route but his mind was on the billionaire—the one only thirty-five miles away in Asheville. He wondered what it would be like to talk to him and if he would learn anything from such a rich man. But Jim knew better than to daydream too much. He knew what the chances were of a small-town teenager ever getting to talk to someone so important. He pedaled and tossed papers like it was second nature for him, still wondering if meeting the guy was ever possible and if so, how? Jim slowed his bike as he came around the last corner across from Thompson's store. He stopped for a moment, used one foot on the ground to balance the bike and remembered what the preacher had said so many years ago: "If God is for you, who can be against you?" With the thought foremost in his mind, he felt a surge of confidence wash through him. Lord willing, there had to be a way to meet the billionaire, and he was determined to find that way. After all he realized, he was now a child of God, and God would help.

In Saluda, there were not a whole lot of choices when it came to communicating with the outside world. There was the phone, the teletype machine and the postal service. That was it, but Jim was in a unique position after working for the Thompsons for two years. He was one of only four people in Saluda who knew how to run the teletype machines. And as much as the wire seemed to be the quickest way to contact someone, he realized that he had only a name and the town of the billionaire and not his wire address. Even if he did, how could he keep from getting caught using the teletype for his own personal business? It could be risky putting his job and character on the line. Even though his mind was full of ideas, he could not think of a successful plan. Finally, he decided that after work, he would go fishing to see if any ideas popped into his head.

Jim made it home early from work that afternoon while it was still light outside. He was still thinking about how to make contact with the billionaire. He left his books on the kitchen table, hurried out the back door to the shed, picked up his fishing pole and stringer, and decided that today he would go fishing at his favorite fishing hole just across the valley. He stopped to dig for worms under the sunflowers where he could always count on finding the fattest and juiciest worms—a sure-fire feast for even the most discriminating fish. He dumped both worms and dirt into a paper bag, grabbed his poles and hurried to his trusty secret fishing spot.

Oak trees canopied around the edge of the pond, casting shadows across the water. Jim sat down on his familiar clump of moss and pulled an earthworm from the paper bag. He looked at the slimy, cool, wiggling worm and wondered why fish were so attracted to worms. He put the worm on the hook and with a flick of his wrist tossed the baited worm and bobber into a shady little nook along the bank and waited for his bobber to move. It was then that his thoughts started to form with new strategy. Bait, he wondered, what kind of bait would he need to use for a billionaire? What does a billionaire want? What does he need? What is good bait? His thoughts were interrupted by a quick downward movement of the bobber. He instinctively jerked his pole, but no fish, just half a worm still dangling there.

After the first hour, Jim sat staring at the water, bored and unsatisfied with no new ideas. And since the fish weren't biting, he pulled the *Farmers' Almanac* out of his knapsack and started flipping through the pages. A particular section caught his attention. It was a section devoted to "top ten" lists. As he scanned the page, he noticed one particular list about what people wanted most. Number one on the list was the need to feel important. Jim had never particularly felt important. Getting picked on most of his young life had left him feeling unacceptable and, beyond the small world he and his mother shared, he could think of very little that helped him feel important. For a few minutes he just stared at the ground, lost in his own thoughts. If he wanted to meet the billionaire and the one thing people wanted most was to feel important, he figured he had to find out what was important to the billionaire. But, how he could possibly make a billionaire feel more important than he already was, the young man wondered. He pulled the newspaper out of his knapsack searching for answers. Again, he read the headline, "New York Billionaire Moves To Asheville Amidst Scandal." As he read the lines over and over, he locked in on the word, scandal. His thoughts were scrambled with unanswered questions, with guessing about a world that was totally unknown to him. He knew about small town gossip but what could a person with so much money have done wrong to create a scandal? There must be another side to the article but what could it be.

Then Jim remembered how he had been ridiculed and picked on and how bad he had felt just because he didn't know his natural father. He reasoned that maybe the billionaire was getting picked on because he was different or because people weren't taking time to understand him. Jim realized that a plan was forming and he made a decision to send the billionaire a telegram when he got back to the store. He pulled out his writing notebook and started to compose a message.

Jim got to the general store the next afternoon and was excited. He had made up his mind to use the store's teletype machine to wire a message to the billionaire. He wondered if the man would respond. He wondered why he would respond to a young teenager from the hills. He had worked with the telegraph for only a year, but he had learned quickly and developed a rather sophisticated understanding of how the wires were routed and delivered. He decided that he would contact the hub router and get the appropriate number where to wire the message. He would say it involved an important financial matter. Although he doubted that others would agree with him, Jim rationalized that buying a billionaire a sundae was an important financial matter. When he contacted the hub router, he got the address and was able to wire the message before Mrs. Thompson returned to the store.

Several days went by, days turned into weeks and no answer from his wire. Jim decided that something must have gone wrong. His first thought was that perhaps the billionaire had not seen his wire. So he decided that he would continue wiring a new message every other day. Three months went by and still no reply. Of course, Jim had no way of knowing that the billionaire's office had not been amused and, in fact, wired back on one occasion that all such messages should stop immediately. Undaunted, Jim rationalized that the billionaire just hadn't had a chance to read the messages he had sent with the teletype since office staff kept intercepting them.

Another week passed before it all caught up with him. After school, when he walked into the store to start his shift at work, the first thing he saw was Mrs. Thompson and Sheriff Miller standing at the counter. Both turned to Jim and watched as he walked toward them. He smiled and nodded politely as he headed to his work station. But Mrs. Thompson grabbed his arm as he walked by.

"Jim, you should be ashamed of yourself." Her voice was stern and her face looked mean, quite unlike her usual manner. "If she wasn't sick, I would call your mother and tell her to take a switch to you."

"What are you talking about?" he asked. Jim, wide-eyed and caught off guard, shifted anxiously.

"You know exactly what I am talking about, young man," she said. "You have been sending wires to Mr. Robert Hudson without permission."

Sheriff Miller stepped in with a much softer tone and began to question the young man.

"Jim, I know you're young, son," he said. "But if you don't stop sending the wires, you could find yourself up on harassment charges and then I'd have to run you in."

"Cat got your tongue, boy," asked Mrs. Thompson, not backing off a whit. "Put on that apron and you pick up that broom and start doing what I pay you for. And you better stop this nonsense or you'll be looking for another job."

Jim looked at the floor, disheartened and relieved at the same time. He still had his job and he wasn't in jail. For that he was grateful. But he also knew that he was more determined than ever to get to Mr. Hudson. For reasons not yet clear to Jim, he believed whole-heartedly that Mr. Hudson would like him, that through meeting the man, Jim would have a chance at a better life than he and his mother had known.

All that afternoon, he swept, stocked, and kept busy with whatever he thought Mrs. Thompson would like done. And as deliberately as he worked, he worked in his mind to find a way to talk to the billionaire. Late in the day it hit him. What if he wrote Mr. Hudson a letter and ran it in the paper as an ad he thought. Certainly then someone would show the ad to the billionaire. He knew he had managed to save forty-nine dollars working at Thompson's, but he also knew that he had no idea how much it would cost to run such an ad. He needed to find out, but first the letter he decided. In his letter, Jim chose his words carefully trying to share his feelings with Mr. Hudson.

Dear Mr. Hudson:

I'm a 16-year-old boy in Saluda, NC. Maybe you haven't heard of it before, but I'm right across the mountain from you. I deliver papers here in town and saw an article written about you in the "Saluda-Hendersonville News & Times."

Anyways, I just want to say not to let those people who are saying bad things get to you. I know how it feels to be different. The way I figure it, with you being a billionaire and all, that makes you kind of different too, not like us ordinary folks. I guess you're getting picked on because you got something they don't. I figure since you're smart enough to make a billion dollars, I also figure you are smart enough not to do what the newspaper says you might have done. I figure they're just looking for someone different to start rumors about. Don't worry, people do that to me, too, and I don't have but $49 bucks saved.

You don't know me from Adam, Mr. Hudson, but I just wanted to tell you how I get through the tough times when people are picking on me. My pastor once told me that I'm a child of God and if I'm good enough for God, I don't care what the people have to say about me. You're a child of God too, if you chose to be, just a grown-up one, I guess. And so my question is this, if God is for you, who can be against you?

Well, I've said enough so welcome to Asheville and if you ever make it over to Saluda, please come in the Thompson's General Store and say hello. That's where I work after school as a clerk and with a little of that money I have saved up, I'll buy you an ice cream sundae. One of those always makes me feel better no matter what's bothering me.

Sincerely,

Jim Smith

When he found out the cost of the ad, over fifteen dollars and almost a third of his savings, Jim knew he was taking a chance but the ad would be worth it he hoped. Besides, he thought he might learn something from the billionaire that would help him make his money back. More determined than ever, Jim mailed his letter to the paper.

At first the editor did not take the letter seriously, but after a quick phone call to Jim and some brief discussion, the editor told Jim he'd run it. It was set to run the following week in Friday's paper. When that day rolled around, Jim was out of bed and dressed in matter of minutes. He kissed his mother and told her how much he loved her. He told her that it was a very special day and that he could not wait to share a surprise with her later. He bicycled into town with all the speed he could muster. His only thought was today he would get Mr. Hudson's attention.

At the general store, he ripped the brown paper wrapping around the stack of news papers. As he tore through the paper looking for his ad, he imagined Mr. Hudson reading his letter over his morning coffee. He scanned every page looking for his letter. Seconds of anticipations were turning into what seemed like minutes for Jim. It has to be here, he thought. He had invested, but would it pay-off, he wondered. Finally, he saw the page, bold and printed with his words. Apparently, the publisher had been so touched by the letter that he had published it as a full-page ad on the back of the last page of the business section.

"Wow!" Jim exclaimed as his teenage heart raced with excitement.

Jim was so excited. He could hardly wait for school to be out so he could run down to the lumber mill where his mother worked in the office. The hours ticked by slowly as Jim waited for school to be out. And then it happened. A knock at the classroom door and a note was given to his teacher, Ms. Williams. His teacher read the note and looked up at Jim. She asked Jim if she could talk with him outside of the classroom and for him to bring his books. Outside the classroom, Ms. Williams was joined by Sheriff Miller.

"Jim I need you to come with me, son," Sheriff Miller said, "Your mom collapsed today at work and she was rushed to the hospital over in Hendersonville. I want to run you over there."

The ride was a short few miles that seemed to take forever. Sheriff Miller and Jim walked into the hospital and gave the receptionist his mom's name. She picked up the phone and called to get her room. As she asked her voice suddenly change and her eyes withdrew. "Mr. Smith, they are waiting for you down this hall room 3b," she said with a heartbroken stare. Jim didn't understand her facial expressions, but walked down the hall she directed him and read each door for 3b. He entered the room and saw a nurse and doctor standing in front of the bed. Behind them he saw his mother lying in the bed.

"Jim?" asked the nurse.

"Yes," said Jim.

Her eyes filled with tears and she said, "Honey, I don't know how to tell you this but your mother just passed away." She reached out with loving and sympathetic arms to try to comfort the boy.

Jim stopped. Jim had heard what she had said, but couldn't quite process it. He felt a lump in his throat as tears filled his eyes. He pushed past the nurse's outstretched arms to his mother.

"Mama....mama...wake up mama. Mama. Mama! Wake-up! Maaaama...Nooo!" Jim grabbed his mothers limp cold hand, the warm hand that had loved him for so many years, and collapsed to his knees and began to weep in agony. As Jim wept, the doctor tried futilely to explain what had happened and how her lung had collapsed from scar tissue, but Jim heard nothing. He felt utterly lost.

The funeral was small. Mrs. Thompson and Mrs. Jacobs helped Jim with the arrangements. Jim's mother had managed to secure a small insurance policy that almost covered the price of the funeral.

For next two weeks, Jim felt empty and lonely. He hurt. Mrs. Thompson was concerned about him being all alone. Jim assured her he would be okay and was confident that God would see him through. Mrs. Thompson knew he would be 17 soon and was a very responsible and capable young man. Yet, still she worried.

Weeks passed and Jim had forgotten all about the letter he had placed in the newspaper. Jim sat on the front porch of Thompson's General store rolling his liberty silver dollar between his two thumbs and index fingers and then he remembered the letter in the paper. He had heard nothing. He believed in what he had done, but maybe he was being a little foolish in thinking a man like Mr. Hudson would actually care about his letter? He stared at the silver dollar that he rolled between his fingers and read again those four powerful words that had started him out so many years ago, "In God We Trust." A lot had happened and although he was in a lot of pain, he still had an unction that maybe what he had done wasn't so silly. Maybe it would work. Jim knew God was for him so he would just wait.

Another two weeks passed and still no answer. It was Friday afternoon, February 23, 1951, Jim's first birthday without his mother and his hope for hearing from the billionaire had all but vanished. He was going to have Saturday off and was looking forward to a leisurely day of fishing to celebrate his seventeenth birthday. He arrived at Thompson's after school and walked by the soda fountain as he did every day, to put on his apron. Out of the corner of his eye he noticed a gentlemen sitting at the soda fountain bar. He was different looking unlike most of Thompson's customers. For one thing, he was dressed in a dark grey pinstriped suit and polished wing-tip shoes with a smart hat that sat upon the soda counter beside him. Jim had not seen too many people dressed in suits, but from what he had seen in mail-order catalogs at Thompson's, he figured a suit like that must be expensive.

All of a sudden, Jim felt the adrenalin rush as his knees weakened, his stomach sank, and his heart pounded, rendering him totally motionless. At the same time, Mrs. Thompson rounded the corner nearly bumping into him.

"Oh, Jim, there you are," she smiled. "You have a visitor at the fountain counter, says his name is Hudson, Robert Hudson," she said. With a sly grin and a quick wink, she disappeared into the stockroom.

Jim took off his apron, folded it neatly and laid it carefully on a box inside the stock room. Then he walked slowly behind the fountain counter trying to restrain both his excitement and fear. He instinctively took a deep breath, extended his right hand, and looked the billionaire right in the eye. "Hello, my name is Jim Smith," he said.

Firmly gripping Jim's hand and smiling warmly, the gentlemen responded, "Well, Jim, it's good to meet you. My name is Robert, Robert Hudson," Mr. Hudson said. "That is quite a firm grip you have there young man," he said with a wink.

"Mr. Hudson, excuse me if you will, but I have dreamed of meeting you for more than a year," Jim stammered. "Now, I can't believe that you are sitting right here in front of me."

"Well, Mr. Jim Smith, may I call you Jim?" said Mr. Hudson.

"Yes, ah, I mean, yes sir, Mr. Hudson. Jim would be just swell."

"Well, Jim," Mr. Hudson smiled. "I wanted to see the young man who has more persistence than virtually anyone I know. I have had people try to track me down for a lot of things, but nothing quite like this. I must admit that your letter published in the paper sure did get my attention."

"Mr. Hudson, I apologize about…." Jim tried to explain.

"Shhhh," the man whispered and then continued. "The first rule is do not apologize for something you really want to do. My old friend,

Henry Ford, used to say, 'Don't explain and don't complain.' Now, what do you say we sit right here and get to know each other?"

The two of them sat talking for almost two hours. Mrs. Thompson had given her smile of approval each time she walked by and Jim found himself almost hypnotized by the conversation.

"I tell you what, Jim," he said, "why don't we go ask your parents what their plans are for the weekend, because I would like to invite you all up to my house in Asheville this Sunday."

"Mr. Hudson, it's just me now. My mamma passed away 5 weeks ago and she was my only family," Jim said painfully. "I would love to come, but there is only one problem."

"Jim I am so sorry to hear about your mother," Hudson said empathetically. "What's the one problem though?" Mr. Hudson asked.

"It's my car, it's not too good and might not make it," Jim continued. "There's a chance I could borrow Mrs. Thompson's delivery truck," he thought out loud. "I'll find a way though."

"I bet you will find a way and I like the way you said that," Hudson said. "But let me help you out there. Why don't I have my driver come and pick you up? You know us children of God are usually wrapped up Sunday mornings, but what do you say I have my driver pick you up around 1:30 p.m.?"

"That would be great!" said Jim.

"Do you like to fish, son?" Hudson asked.

"Boy, do I ever," he answered.

"Well, that's great then, because I have just opened up three new trout ponds on my property and my manager tells me they should be just about ready to fish this weekend. If it's no too cold outside, we'll have a go at it and see what we can reel in," smiled Hudson.

"We'll be ready and thank you so much Mr. Hudson," Jim answered.

"It'll cost you," grinned Mr. Hudson. "What do you say buying me that ice cream sundae you promised? It's a mighty warm here in the store and that would hit the spot."

"One ice cream sundae...correction, the best ice cream sundae in the Carolinas coming right up." Jim said, grinning with elation and pride.

What Do Wealthy People Do?

"To Become Successful Quickly, Do What Successful People Do!"
Andrew Carnegie

It was unlike any Sunday morning Jim had ever experienced; he was going to visit Mr. Hudson today and now could hardly wait to get home from church. Mrs. Thompson helped him by having his very best clothes cleaned and pressed. He had made sure that his shoes were shined and Mrs. Jacobs trimmed his hair. He had thanked them both with a big hug; he had still wished his mother could have joined him on his trip to Asheville. He had barely slept two winks the night before and the thought of going to Mr. Hudson's almost seemed like a dream.

It was one-thirty exactly when Jim heard the sound of gravel crunching under wheels of a car in the distance. The sound could only mean one thing; and then he saw it slowly rolling toward the house. The long black car was much bigger than he expected. Even though he had read about limousines, seeing the real thing was hard for him to believe. He had never seen a car this big, and as far as limousines go, he couldn't imagine seeing one bigger let alone riding in one. As the huge car came to a slow stop in front of his cabin, Jim was reminded of how tiny the cabin was that he and his mother had called home. Nevertheless, he was awfully proud of how his mother had made what little they had into a warm and loving home.

With a huge smile that he could barely contain, Jim quickly opened the door. He stepped out onto the porch smoothing his shirt, pressing a stray hair in place. The driver, a handsome, older gentlemen dressed in a black hat and a sharply pressed black suit, had walked toward the front porch.

"Hello. My name is Charles McConner and I am the driver for Mr. Robert Hudson," he said. He walked with a bounce, smiled broadly, and spoke with a heavy Scottish brogue. "I am here to pick up a Mr. Jim Smith."

"I am Jim Smith," he said as he extended his hand and shook Mr. McConner's hand.

"A pleasure to meet you, Mr. Smith," the driver said.

"Oh, yes, sir, my pleasure too," Jim said, shaking his hand.

"Mr. Hudson has instructed me to take you to his home in Asheville," the driver said. "Oh, yes, me lad, let me think. Ah, Mr. Hudson wanted me to remind you to bring some warm work clothes suitable for fishing. I think he is intending to take you to his newest pond."

With that, Jim was in and out of the house in a flash with his extra clothes. As Mr. McConner held the door for them, Jim climbed through the doorway of the beautifully polished limousine. The smell of leather mixed with the fragrance of a dozen roses beautifully arranged in a stunning crystal vase was all but intoxicating to Jim. Mr. McConner slipped into the driver's seat and turned around speaking to Jim.

"Please feel free to enjoy a drink if you like," he said. "There is fresh squeezed orange and grapefruit juice and sparkling water in the beverage compartments. Fresh strawberries and pastries are on the server."

"Gee, thanks, Mr. McConner," said Jim.

"You are quite welcome, lad. You see, Mr. Hudson personally saw to it that you have the best during this ride," the driver answered just before he pulled the privacy glass closed.

Although the thirty-five miles to Asheville took almost an hour, the ride seemed to take only moments. At some point, he finally relaxed enough to nibble on the berries and pastries. He thought of his mom. Jim was still feeling like he was in a dream when he leaned over and whispered to the memory of his mom, "Mom, the Lord sure has blessed us. Thanks for putting a good word in for me." But, when he saw the sign that said "Asheville—5 miles," he realized that everything around him was, in fact, very real.

Reaching the outskirts of the mountain town, the limousine began to slow and finally approached a driveway entrance lined with beautifully manicured English boxwoods.

"Wow!" Jim said. "I have never seen anything like this before," he continued talking to himself.

Jim shook her head. He struggled to understand the wealth and beauty he was looking at. The limousine had traveled only a short distance when they came upon a massive stone archway with two enormous gates. The gates slowly opened, allowing Mr. McConner to drive through and continue down the drive. He then reached back and opened the privacy glass.

"You are now entering Mr. Hudson's estate," he said. "Welcome to Lion's Gate."

Jim could think of no words to describe the beauty that he saw. They were silent as the limousine gently rolled forward and then gracefully began its track down a beautiful winding drive. Dense towering spruce trees lined one side of the drive and a mountain stream flowed down the other side. The mile-long drive seemed to go on in slow motion as if they had traveled many more miles than the one.

Two large twenty foot iron gates opened on either side of the drive. As the limousine navigated between the two gates, the sun illuminated a huge yard and reflective pool. And there it was—the house. Jim couldn't believe what he was actually seeing. This was no house. This was a castle. He had only seen things like this in books. It was truly stunning. As the car approached the large entrance way, Jim became transfixed on a huge Hudson family seal engraved into the granite entrance way above two large oak doors.

"Welcome to Lion's Gate," said Mr. McConner. "This is Mr. Hudson's home. There are about four acres of floor space in all, a truly magnificent estate. I can't remember a time when I have approached the house from the front drive where my breath wasn't taken way. No, my boy, ya can't see anything like it here in America, ya have to go to France or me home Scotland to find anything so grand."

Mr. McConner steered the limousine and followed the circular driveway around to the front entrance. Mr. Hudson's butler, Mr. Timmins, met Jim at the enormous entry door. The butler escorted him into the foyer and asked Jim to follow him to an adjoining keeping room. The entry foyer was tiled with black and white travertine marble that swirled in three dimensional helixes and above it all a ceiling that seemed to be a hundred feet high, painted with beautiful, graceful angels. As they made their way across the entrance, Jim noticed that his footsteps echoed in the great hall. On the right was an arboretum with tropical trees and plants the likes Jim had only seen in books. To the left, Mr. Timmins opened a set of pocket doors for Jim to enter the octagonal keeping room.

"Please make yourself comfortable while you wait," Mr. Timmins said. "Mr. Hudson should be with you momentarily."

The butler nodded toward a red velvet Victorian sofa. Jim sat down and began looking around in awe at the enormous room. Eighteenth century oil painted portraits hung on richly paneled walls, luxuriously woven draperies framed the windows. Sun-light reflected off the crystal chandelier making the light seem to dance above them. Jim could not resist touching the heavy window curtains that seemed to billow over the arm of the sofa. A few minutes passed.

The pocket doors quietly slid open again. A smallish man wearing spectacles and a warm smile entered the room.

"You must be Mr. Jim Smith," he said. "My name is Robert Friedman, Mr. Hudson's personal assistant. It's a pleasure to meet you," he said, extending his hand in greeting. "Mr. Hudson has been looking forward to your visit. He asked that I bring you to his personal library. Mr. Hudson has a love for roses and will take you from the library to his conservatory to show you his newest varieties."

Jim followed Mr. Friedman through a grand hall that was adorned by massive tapestries on either side.

"Another passion of Mr. Hudson's, sixteenth and seventeenth century Flemish tapestries," Mr. Friedman said as he pointed to his left and right. At the end of the long, impressive hall, they approached tall arched wooden doors. Mr. Friedman flung the doors open revealing a library and study with two floors of bookshelves filled to the brim with hundreds of books. A spiral staircase connected the two floors. Above, the ceiling was a circular dome painted with more exquisite reliefs. A heavy gothic iron chandelier hung from the center of the dome.

"Mr. Hudson will be here soon," Friedman explained, "but in the meantime, Jim, I understand that Mr. Hudson is taking you fishing today," Friedman said with a wink and a smile

Friedman excused himself and Jim slowly began looking intently at the books on the shelves, walking around pulling out a book here and there. How could he ever have imagined he would wind up here in the library of one of the nation's wealthiest men—a library that was bigger than their whole house?

"Welcome," said Robert Hudson with open arms and a huge inviting smile. Over his clothes, he wore a green apron and held a pair of gardening gloves in his hand. Jim spun around, startled by Mr. Hudson's sudden appearance and hearty greeting.

"Hi, Mr. Hudson!" Jim said with excitement.

"Mr. Hudson, you shocked me," Jim said. "I didn't even see you come in."

"Well, Jim, that is why I asked Robert to bring you in here into my library," Hudson said. When I was a boy, I always wanted to have a secret passage and now I have many, but I wanted to show you my favorite. Do you see that light green book behind my desk on the third shelf up?" he asked. "Go over and pull it out, son."

Jim went over and carefully examined the spine of a green book titled <u>The Science of Getting Rich</u>. He reached to pull it from the shelf, but only the top pulled forward. The bottom of the book seemed to be fixed to a hinge of some sort and as Jim pulled the green book forward from the shelf, a panel moved behind Hudson's desk, and a doorway opened as quiet as a whisper.

"Come on," Hudson smiled and with child-like excitement motioned to Jim to follow.

They followed him down a stone spiral staircase. Moist and warm air smelled like a fresh spring rain. As Jim followed Hudson, daylight began to penetrate the dark. At the bottom of the staircase, the two walked into a spacious glass-enclosed greenhouse where they were met by the fragrant smell of roses that permeated the atrium. An indoor stream of water tumbled across the rocks while beautiful tropical trees, bountiful with fruit, cast an impressionistic work of shadow and light across the rose bushes.

"Welcome to my conservatory," he said. "It was originally the Duke of Hampshire's, but I bought it and had it disassembled and brought here from England. By now you may have notice, I like roses. Roses are a lot like achieving success, as you start at the bottom you have to make it through a few well positioned thorns

39

before you make it to the blossom or, as I like to say, the fragrance and beauty of life. Jim, come let me show you my favorite. This is the Grey Pearl. It is quite rare. They say it is most difficult to grow, yet in my thinking it is the easiest. You just have to know the secret."

"I'd like to share the secret with you a little later," Hudson continued. "Jim as I mentioned to you back in Saluda you are quite a young man."

"I know you just lost your mother last month and Mrs. Thompson told my assistant that you are pretty much living on your own. Is that right?" he asked.

"Yes that is right. I have had a few people like Mrs. Thomson and Mrs. Jacobs offer me a room in their home, but I have decided to keep the old place and just make the best of it," Jim said.

"Well Jim since you are the head of the house now, with your permission and blessing, I'd like to teach you everything I wish someone would have taught me at your age. I would like to become your mentor...your teacher."

Jim felt his breath catch for a moment while he waited to process what he just had heard. He still couldn't believe it. More than anything, he wanted to learn how to be the best man he possibly could be. Jim then replied, "Yes I would love to have you show me and would consider it an honor."

"Well, son, we have a lot to talk about," Hudson said with a hearty laugh. "Let's go back upstairs to my library and discuss your future," he said as he removed his gardening apron.

In the library, Robert Hudson sat at his massive mahogany desk facing Jim. Jim sat across from Mr. Hudson in a tufted-leather wingback chair.

"Jim, I am excited about trying out my new fishing stream a little later. It has been stocked full of some of the healthiest rainbow trout you ever have seen," said Hudson with a warm smile. "But to be quite honest with you, I didn't invite you up here just to go fishing with me. No, sir, I invited you because you impressed me with what you did in the paper and you impressed me even more with your persistence," he continued. "I don't believe I was too much older than you when my dad first introduced me to Mr. Andrew Carnegie, the great steel baron from Pittsburgh, Pennsylvania. Mr. Carnegie was a friend of my dad and was like a second father to me. He taught me quite a bit. But about persistence he would always say this: 'Robert, never forget, persistence is to a man's character as carbon is to steel. Find persistence and you've found your man.'"

Mr. Hudson continued to explain that he believed that Jim was made up of something really special.

"Jim, if you would allow me, I would like to help develop those special gifts," Hudson said as he smiled. "Now, I believe you just celebrated your seventeenth birthday. Isn't that correct?"

"Yes, sir," Jim replied.

"And you are living on your own now. Is that correct too?

"Yes, sir," Jim replied again.

"Well, perhaps you will think of what I'm about to offer as a birthday gift on such a day for you. Jim I would like to send you to visit a few of my friends to learn the secrets of becoming wealthy," he said. "Now, I know through Mrs. Thompson you have Easter vacation coming up here in a few weeks from school and I wanted to see if you could go, all expenses paid, to visit three of my closest friends in Boston, Chicago and Dallas. Jim I will make sure that one of my personal managers will be there to help attend to your every need."

Jim was excited. "I will do it," he exclaimed again. He knew that he had never been away from home for any length of time, but he realized that God had arranged this meeting not by accident, but rather by Divine design. Jim felt as if his mother was somehow watching and smiling over this great news. He was elated and felt like he would burst at the seams with excitement.

"Well, now, that's fantastic," Hudson said. "And Jim, I think we have some fishing to do, don't we?"

Just as Jim was about to answer, Mrs. Hudson walked into the room. Her husband beamed with loving pride as he introduced Caroline Hudson.

"I would like to introduce the most special woman I know, my wife, Caroline."

"He is still just as charming as the day I met him," Caroline interrupted.

Jim put out his hand to shake Mrs. Hudson's.

"Hi. My name is Jim Smith," he said.

"Mr. Smith, I am very glad to meet you," she answered, shaking his hand. "Robert, correct me if I am wrong, but I believe you were about to take our young guest fishing over at your newest trout stream, am I right?"

"You are correct, my dear, as always" he said.

"Well, then you two go and have fun fishing," she said with a warm smile.

The Wealth of Thought

"Thoughts are things, things have gravity and gravity attracts.
What are your thoughts attracting into your life?"

Jon Bender

Jim noticed that even though more than two weeks had passed since he spent the afternoon with Mr. Hudson; it seemed like yesterday that they had been talking and fishing. Now he found himself in an airport for the first time. The terminal was unfamiliar to him, rather strange but exciting at the same time. He looked forward to his first flight but even more, he looked forward to learning all that Mr. Hudson had promised.

"Ladies and gentleman, we will now board all rows for Piedmont Airlines flight 158 to Washington National." The message came over the gate intercom and Jim knew it was time for the journey to begin.

Once he was on the plane, he sat back with a huge smile on his face trying to take in all that was happening to him. He was on a small DC-3 airplane going to a new and exciting city—quite a departure from his simple day-to-day way of life of going to school and working at Thompson's each day.

The flight was smooth and when they arrived at Washington National, Jim quickly deplaned and experienced the hustle and bustle of a modern terminal. He found his gate and after a short wait boarded his American Airlines flight to Boston. Nearing the Boston area, from the window of the DC-7, Jim could see the skyline of Boston on the approach to the airport. The city below him looked big with all the buildings but especially small from the sky. He marveled at the beauty of the harbor islands as he approached.

Mr. Hudson had made arrangements for Jim to meet one of his dearest friends, Miss Jane Nelson. Hudson had met Jane ten years earlier when Jane was a young sales representative for a company Mr. Hudson's company did business with. Having a female sales representative in the chemical industry was quite unusual, but Robert Hudson never paid much attention to "boy's club" stereotypes. However, he did pay attention to Jane and recognized something in her that was very special. Hudson had noticed that out of all the representatives from other companies, Jane was the most "good finding." Not only had she never said anything negative or disparaging about any of her competitors, but she actually praised her competitors. Jane seemed to have a personality that looked for what was good in everything along with an attitude of where and how she could help create more good. Caroline, who worked with Hudson during those years, met Jane and was also immediately attracted to her contagious optimism and creative spirit. Caroline asked Hudson if he would begin giving business advice to Jane. She argued that it was difficult if not almost impossible for a woman to make it in a male-dominated business and she believed Jane deserved every advantage possible.

Jane learned quickly and excelled with her attitude and creativity. She quickly became the top representative for her company. Within three years under Mr. and Mrs. Hudson's tutelage, Jane had organized investors to buy a competitive Swiss company that made chemicals including advanced naturopathic medicine and natural supplements. She was convinced of the healing power of nature and was passionate about bringing the human body into natural balance. She was equally convinced that western health care would dramatically decline as more and more people looked for antibiotic-style "magic" bullets. She was convinced that the institutionalization of medicine led by large profit pharmaceutical companies would eventually degrade health care into nothing more than disease care by the end of the 20th century in the U.S. and Canada.

Jane led her new company to banner sales and created product lines that educated her customers and focused on supplying the best in health care rather than disease care. Within five years under her leadership, the company grew to the world's largest nutritional supplement company of its type. The company had annual sales at $7 million and began leading the field in her fledging industry.

So on that day when Jim arrived in Boston, he was looking forward to meeting with Mr. Hudson's friends. He picked up his tattered leather satchel loaned to him by Mrs. Thompson and followed other passengers off the plane. As he walked into the Boston airport terminal, he scanned the gate area. His attention was immediately called to a well-dressed gentleman holding a sign that read, "Mr. Jim Smith." Beside the well-dressed man was a beautiful woman. She was dressed in a smart deep navy blue business suit and stylish black pumps. Her auburn hair was pulled up and she wore trendy horn rimmed glasses.

"You must be our Mr. Jim Smith," said the woman.

Jim nodded.

"My name is Jane Nelson and this is Mr. Wilcox," she said, extending her hand. "I am very glad to meet you. Mr. Hudson has told me a lot about you," she said with an approving smile.

"I am very happy to meet you Miss Nelson." He noticed her very strong handshake. "And you, too, Mr. Wilcox," he said, shaking his hand.

"Did you have a nice flight?" asked Jane.

"Yes it was amazing. This was my first time flying and it was really swell."

Miss Nelson laughed as they turned toward the baggage area. She began telling him about her first flight. As they walked, she asked him about his home, and his school.

When Jim attempted to grab his small suitcase from the baggage cart, Mr. Wilcox stepped in and respectfully took it from Jim's hand, carrying the bag as they all found their way out of the airport.

"Wow, what a car!" Jim exclaimed.

Waiting curbside for them was a white stretch limousine. Jane and Jim disappeared into its luxury when Mr. Wilcox opened the passenger door for them.

"Do all rich people drive limousines?" asked Jim.

Jane laughed and said, "You know I asked the same question when I met Mr. Hudson for the first time. Actually, having a car like this can be very handy in business and the best part is when you own your own company. Your company can pay for it," she said.

"So what you mean is the company owns the car, but you get to ride in it whenever you want?" Jim asked.

"Something like that, Jim," said Jane. "Now, I have a room booked for you in my favorite hotel here in Boston. It's called the Ritz-Carlton and has been here since 1927. I have spoken to the management and they have been instructed to take care of anything you need or want," she said with a smile.

"Miss Nelson, you didn't have to go to so much trouble for me," Jim replied.

"Oh don't give it a thought, Jim, it was no trouble at all, and please call me Jane," she said. "We have a big day ahead of us tomorrow and a lot of things to talk about. When we get to the hotel,

I want you to get a good night's rest and I will meet you here at the hotel at 7:30 a.m. for breakfast, okay?"

"That sounds terrific Miss Nels...I mean Jane,"

Jim took one look at his room and immediately checked the door again to make sure it was the right room. He had not seen nor imagined a hotel room so large and luxurious. The room opened into a huge marble entry foyer. A staircase with gold banisters led up to the bedroom. Two French doors opened into the bedroom. From the palladium windows, he could see Boston's City Garden and historic Newbury Street.

He finally walked over to the massive four poster bed and let his small body sink into the thick feather-filled duvet. A childish excitement came over him and he kicked off his shoes and began jumping and bouncing on the bed only to collapse once again in the feeling of luxury as he slipped into the cool crisp sheets of his bed. In less than ten minutes, he was sleeping soundly.

Jim woke well rested and full of energy and excitement for the day ahead of him. He met Jane at 7:30 a.m. sharp in the lobby.

"I am so glad that you have come to Boston," Jane told him. "Mr. Hudson has been full of praises for you and asked if I would share some of the things I had learned on my personal path to success. I felt honored that he would call because it wasn't so many years ago he helped me begin to think and do business in a certain way. I believe what he taught me has largely been responsible for my success," she said.

"Jim, I wanted to start by teaching you the first thing Robert Hudson taught me," she continued. "It is a universal law. That means it doesn't work some of the time, it works ALL of the time. If you remember what I am about to tell you, if you burn it into your memory and let it sink into your heart, you will have a simple, but powerful foundation to build great wealth, and I am not just talking about money. Rather, I am talking about real wealth which includes money, relationships, health, vitality, and most of all, gratitude," she said. "Robert told me this: 'Thoughts are things, things have gravity and gravity attracts.' And then he asked *what my thoughts were attracting into my life.* I learned that there is a lifetime of wisdom in that simple question."

Jane and Jim continued to talk. She told Jim that if he would write those words down and read them daily that he would begin his pathway to true wealth immediately. Jane shared her background with him and he told her a little about himself. Then she shared her divinely inspired wisdom with the young man.

"Most people think about becoming wealthy, yet most get neither financial wealth nor any other kind of wealth because they never discover this little known secret about how the world really works."

"What do you mean when you say, 'how the world really works'?" asked Jim.

"Our world in which we live is nothing more than an infinite opportunity. Have you ever heard the statement, 'As a man thinketh in his heart, so is he?" she asked.

"Yes, I think I've heard my pastor say that before," he answered.

"That's right, Jim, it is from the Bible in the book called Proverbs. In fact, the book of Proverbs was written by one of the wealthiest men ever to live, King Solomon. You can also find variations of these same words in hundreds of other texts spanning nearly four thousand years in history. You see, Jim, opportunity is always around you. As a result, real wealth is always around you. But you must learn how to recognize it, how to tune in to the opportunities."

"Kind of like a radio?" he asked.

"Exactly," she said. "Any thought that you dwell on and have absolute faith that it is on its way to you that very minute will make you in a sense 'magnetized'. In effect, what you are thinking about will be drawn to you through physical channels such as people, situations and/or circumstances. I know when you first hear this it may sound like some far-fetched, metaphysical mumbo-jumbo, but basically it is really simple. What you focus and dwell on the most is what you mostly get. Let me give you an example.

Jim, remember when you first heard of Robert Hudson? Well, correct me if I am wrong, but you read about him in the paper and made a decision that you were going to meet him, right?"

"Right!" he answered.

"You weren't just interested in meeting him, rather you made a *real* decision to meet him, and by definition a *real* decision means cutting yourself off from any uncertainty of doing what you have decided to do. You see, you focused in on the thought of meeting Robert in your mind. You backed it by faith and certainty that you would meet him. You knew you would somehow meet him. You thought about it continuously and did all you could do to meet him. It was at that moment your thoughts became magnetized. Just like gravity, the very thing you thought about—to meet Mr. Hudson—

began to take form and started to be pulled toward you. Does any of this make sense?"

"Yes, it really does, because you are right," he said. "I was very certain that I could meet him. I didn't know how at first. I just knew I would. I just wanted to somehow encourage him, and I knew that God is all for encouraging others. I guess I have never thought about it like this."

But what did you mean when you said, 'real wealth is always around you, but you must learn how to recognize it, how to tune in to the opportunities.' I'm not sure I understand," he said. "I understand how you have to adjust a radio to tune in a radio station, but how does having a particular thought help you get tuned in to what will happen to you?"

"Well, it's not so much getting tuned in to what will happen to you, rather it is getting tuned in to what is happening around you. Let me give you another example. Look around in the restaurant. I want you to focus on every thing you see that is brown. Get a mental image of the things you see and now close your eyes. While keeping your eyes closed, I want you to tell me everything you saw that was green."

"Green?" he asked. "I thought you told me to focus on what was brown."

"I did tell you to focus on what was brown," she said. "But I didn't tell you that you could not see anything else. So, what else did you see—and no peeking."

"Honestly, I don't really recall," Jim said.

"Precisely!" she said. "This is exactly what I meant. You see, Jim, most people react to what happens to them and that is all they see. They never really see what is really around them. When I told you focus on brown, you missed seeing what was green. This is how life is, if you focus on or 'think' mostly about the brown in life, you will never see the green. If you spend your time focusing on everything else, instead of focusing on the things you want most, you'll miss the opportunity for things you want most to be drawn to you through physical channels of people, the circumstances, situations and the opportunities that are always around you. So you see this, really isn't metaphysical at all. It is just a matter of tuning your awareness into what you really want by focusing in and locking-in on it.

Jane told him that most people live their life with no clear goals or an understanding of what they really want. Instead they wander aimlessly around like a boat adrift. If they end up where they want to be, it is completely by accident and as a result their success is meaningless, meaningless in the sense that they can not share with anyone else how to do what they have done. She explained that the secret to success can be distilled down to two simple ideas: decide exactly what it is you want and resolve yourself to pay the price to get it. Jane told him that understanding these ideas was important, but not enough. They needed to be broken down into a usable step-by-step process.

"There are four steps that if followed, will virtually guarantee someone's success," she continued. "There won't be a question of whether or not the follower is successful, rather it will only be a question of when that person is successful. Jim, the instructions are simple. First, imagine that you are in a boat and you are adrift. This is how most people live their lives. Second, you will need to be aware that if you want to go anywhere in life you have to know where you want to go. You have to know precisely in the same way you might chart a course on a map to a specific destination.

"Third, you will need to fix in your mind an exact vision for what you absolutely must have, when you want it, and how it feels to be in possession of it. Let's call this your "desire." You must be crystal clear about what you absolutely want. You must also have a realistic idea by what date you want it. If you can not be clear, then you must get another desire. This is imperative. Again this desire, you hold in your mind must be visualized and emotionalized to start the 'gravitational' pull of physical form of these desires into your life. Additionally, you must have a realistic time frame to accomplish your desire. I suggest you use six months to begin. Once you are clear on what you want to do, have, or become in six months and you can visualize and emotionalize it, this becomes your beacon. This is the thing or the thought you will stay focused on regardless of what else is going on in your life. What you think about most. Just like our little experiment that we did before you will become very aware of those things around you that are moving you closer to your desire. Just like a lighthouse in a stormy sea, this desire will be the thing you keep your mind's eyes on at all costs."

"Fourth, you will need a rudder. Once you have this desire clearly in your mind and you can feel what it is like to have your desire reached, you need to put it down on paper. This will become your rudder. This is so simple because all you will do is take a regular old index card and list in bullet form what you see and feel in your desire. Give yourself exactly seven bullets. Each bullet must be written as, 'I have, I do, I am, I feel...' Many times the bullets of what you will need to realize your desire. For example, I earn $7000 a month. I exercise daily. I am healthy and vital. I feel totally grateful. These bullets are not to be long and drawn out. They are to be to the point. They are to keep you focused through visualizing and emotionalizing your desire."

"So what you are saying, Jane, is that if I can get clear on what I want by seeing it and feeling it, then what I want will act as a lighthouse for me to point my boat toward," said Jim.

"Exactly," said Jane.

"And this index card will help me stay focused," he said. "I guess that's the rudder you are talking about."

"You have what it takes to become very successful," she said. "You are a very good listener. This is a quality of an excellent student. Now that you understand, there is a very important instruction in how to use your rudder," she said. "And that is to keep your proverbial hand on your rudder often," Jane said with a laugh.

"You mean read my card as often as possible," Jim asked.

"And if you don't read your card for a day, what happens?" asked Jane.

"I guess I would be adrift in my boat for a day with no direction."

"And what happens if you don't touch your rudder for a week?"

"I guess I would be lost at sea," he chuckled.

"Jim, let me ask you a question," Jane said smiling. "Wouldn't it be better if you had a navigator or a person holding on to your rudder at all times for you?"

"Yes, but how?"

"Well, we have a conscious as well as a subconscious mind. For example, our subconscious mind controls our breathing, our heartbeat and other bodily functions. But it also houses our emotions, our overall beliefs, and habitual patterns. The subconscious mind acts kind of like an autopilot. Unfortunately for many of us, it is taking us in the wrong direction. The reason for this is that the subconscious is difficult to reach and retrain if you don't know how."

"First it is important to realize the subconscious mind is kind of like a hole with a trap door. This trap door opens and shuts randomly, sometimes when least expected. Whatever is going on at that time enters into the subconscious mind through the trap door. This is why sometimes things get connected with other things that are not logical and fall through the trap door and are stored away in your subconscious. For example, sometimes when I hear a certain song on the radio from my high school years I feel a stab of pain about breaking up with a boyfriend. That was over thirty-five years ago,

60

but apparently while I was upset about the break-up, I was listening to a particular song. This anchored these sad emotions to that song. Now when I hear that song I feel the same emotions without even thinking because it is stored in my subconscious mind.

"Another example is tying your shoe. We have done it enough times that it has entered our subconscious mind or has fallen through the trap door. We all can tie our shoe without even thinking about it consciously.

"Jim, this is where we want to get with your desire. We want to read our desires on our index card or rudder so often that when that trap door flies open those desires fall in our subconscious storage area. Interestingly enough, just like tying shoes, this may take just a few times or it may take many times before the instructions are sufficiently in our subconscious mind, or you might say, before we can tie them without thinking. By reading your card as often as possible, especially in the beginning months, you will increase the probability of your desires falling through the trap door and fixing them in your subconscious mind.

"From there on, you will find your start becoming successful faster than ever; in fact, it will seem to come out of nowhere. This is because your subconscious mind is now working on your desire or primary thought twenty-four hours a day, seven days week. Moreover, the law says thoughts are things, things have gravity, and gravity attracts. The law applies to both subconscious thoughts (autopilot) and conscious thoughts (manual). It doesn't discriminate."

"Wow!" Jim said. "This is incredible. So the more you look at your card, the greater the chance for your desires to enter into your subconscious mind through the trap door and after that your subconscious will work on the thoughts and desires twenty-four hours a day seven days a week without you even being aware of it."

"Jim," Jane continued, "you learn quickly. You just need a few more things before taking off. The next thing you'll need is some juice!"

"Juice?" he asked.

"The juice… the wind, the gas, the movement, the action, even the best rudder is meaningless unless the boat is moving. You have to get a motor, set sail, start rowing, or just plain kick your feet. You do what ever you have to do to start moving, even if it doesn't appear that you are moving quickly. You must have faith, but faith without action is just plain folly."

Jane told Jim that what he had just learned would put him in a small elite group of some of the wealthiest men and women in the world.

"In fact," she joked, "only of few of them actually know that they know the secret you now know. Interestingly enough, Jim, knowing the secret is not a requirement to achieving success. The only requirement is acting upon the secret or doing things in this certain way. And many find this certain way quite by accident."

"Jane, this makes a lot of sense to me. I actually did this by accident when I figured on meeting Mr. Hudson. I mean I didn't write anything down, but I knew exactly why I wanted to reach him and imagined doing it day after day. Knowing now what you told me, I guess it must have slipped through the trap door."

"Jim," she explained, "I think we have all done this at least once or twice in our life by accident. Imagine what it would be like if we did it intentionally to achieve anything we wanted in life?"

Jane explained that what he just learned is so incredibly powerful she likened it to dynamite. She said that in the wrong hands, this powerful skill of focus could be used to destroy things and in the right hands it can be used to build things.

"As you know," she said, "we just finished fighting a war against a "madman" in Germany. You can bet your bottom dollar he thought about what he wanted with great clarity enough times until his terrible ideas, desires and imageries fell through his trap door. Jim, you should always use what you have learned to build and never tear down. Real wealth is created in the service of others rather than at the expense of others. Many wealthy people don't completely understand this skill and will use it to completely and systematically destroy others while thinking that they are just doing good business. Unfortunately, the cost of using this secret skill in this kind of negative way is the inevitable loss of wealth, relationships and possible health.

She explained to Jim that the secret to using this skill successfully was to use it in a spirit of benefiting others. "How can others 'win' by you 'winning'? That would be what the Romans called 'quid pro quo.' We both win, you might say. You should always succeed by building up others, even those that would be against you. This includes not only what you do, but also includes what you say. Remember what Ben Franklin said, 'I will speak all the good I know about everyone, and will speak ill of no one.' This is the principled rudder that made Ben Franklin one of the most loved men in American history. Is it any wonder that he succeeded in the other areas of his life as well?"

"Jane, I can only hope that one day I can be as successful as you."

"Well Jim," she said, looking him squarely in the eyes, "if you understand the magnitude and far reaching effects of what I've just explained to you, someday you will be as successful as you ever wanted to be. Jim, do me a favor. Remember this: The law is true. *Thoughts are things, things have gravity and gravity attracts.* This means you always will get what you focus on clearly and back with faith. But there is one more important facet to this principle.

"It is true you may have most anything you focus on, but you will only keep it long term if it is God's will for you. Some people say that they don't believe in God, but He believes in them and wants people to have real wealth and not just riches. Although you may be able to think and grow rich, do you really want to be the richest man in the graveyard?" she asked. "What I mean is that you can have virtually anything you want through what I have taught you, but at what cost? Mr. Hudson taught me to trust in God and give thanksgiving daily. I would strongly suggest this to you as well. Your highest calling is to seek God's will for you, your purpose. When you focus on your desires, focus on these desires in the spirit of serving and building for others and to the extent that your desires are inline with God's purpose for you, I promise you that you will be wealthy beyond your wildest dreams, not just financially, but spiritually, physically and mentally as well," she said.

"Well, Jim, we have covered so much today. I only hope that this information can positively impact you in the same way it did me when Mr. Hudson first shared it with me. My understanding is that you will be catching a flight later this afternoon to go visit my good friend, David Hoffmann, in Chicago. Is that correct?"

"Yes," he answered. "I believe my flight is at 4:30 pm."

"You will love David. He is such an interesting man and I have learned so much from him. Make sure you give him my love. Well, we have just a few minutes before I call Mr. Wilcox to drive us to the airport. I want to tell you again how impressed I am with you."

"Jane, thank you so much for sharing with me," he said. "You have taught me so much today and if we have just a few minutes, I have taken several pages of notes and I'd love to make sure that I understand what you have taught me today; can I just review what I have down?"

"Well sure Jim," she said. "That would be wonderful."

"Okay, great. Here is what I have down," he said.

Jim's Notes:

- Thoughts are things, things have gravity and gravity attracts. Always ask, "What are my thoughts attracting into my life?"

- Success is built on two main ideas: (1) decide what you absolutely must have and (2) determine the price and resolve yourself to pay it.

- A man or woman becomes what he or she focuses on the most in their heart.

- Most people have no idea where they are going and do not know or understand their purpose.

- You must visualize and emotionalize your desires on paper. Give yourself a specific time to reach them. This becomes your beacon.

- Bulletize your desires on an index card and read it often. You are looking to have your desires fall through the "trap door" of the subconscious mind and be entered into your conscious mind so you can be on autopilot.

- Succeed in service of people by building others with your wins. Look for the win-win situation.

Jim's Notes Continued:

- Seek God's will or purpose for you and work to make sure your goals and desires are done inline with your God-given purpose.

The Wealth Of Gratitude

"One of the most important discoveries in surviving and thriving in any situation is to live in a constant state of gratitude."

Jon Bender

As Jim sat on the plane headed for Chicago, he thought about what he had learned. Jane was wealthy and confident, yet humble. He wondered if he could ever be like her. Jim's eyes were heavy. As he dozed off, he wondered what Mr. Hoffmann would be like.

Mr. David Hoffmann was President of Royal Amsterdam Bank. Mr. Hudson had told Jim that Mr. Hoffman moved his young family from Holland to Chicago just a few years after the end of the World War II. Mr. Hoffmann had built the bank from scratch into one of the largest and fastest growing commercial banking companies in the world.

Jim jumped as the plane bounced onto the runway of Chicago's Midway Airport. As Jim exited the plane, he looked for someone carrying a sign like the one he had seen in Boston, but didn't see one. With his small carry-on bag in his hand, he began to walk toward an information booth.

Just as he approached the booth, a short nicely-dressed gentleman in a tan camel hair overcoat walked up to him. The man wore a charcoal felt plaid hat with a tiny little red feather secured in its black ribbon band.

"Excuse me, son," he said, with a strong accent. "Would you happen to be Mr. James Smith?"

"Yes, I am James Smith."

"Very nice to meet you, Mr. Smith," he said, extending his hand. "I am David Hoffmann."

"Very nice to meet you, Mr. Hoffmann," Jim said. "How did you recognize me?"

"Very easy, my dear boy," Hoffman said. "Bob—I mean Mr. Hudson, told me that you were one of the finest young men he had ever met. And, well, you looked like a fine young man to me," he said. "How was your flight?"

"It was fantastic," Jim told him. "I had never been to a big city and Jane said Chicago was even bigger than Boston."

"It is definitely a big city. How is my wonderful friend, Jane?"

"She is doing very well, and she wanted me to tell you she sends her love," Jim said.

"She is a beautiful and successful lady," Hoffman said. "I admire her greatly and have learned a lot from her. But for now, we have a wonderful dinner reservation at the Berghoff, my favorite restaurant in Chicago. I let my driver have the night off, so I will be driving us in my car. And if we have time, I might take you past a few of our more popular landmarks like Wrigley Field even though we haven't won a series since 1907," he said with a laugh as they walked to baggage claim area. "Ah yes, Chicago is a great city."

"Mr. Hoffmann, I noticed your accent. Do you mind my asking where you are from?" asked Jim.

"Not at all, my boy," he said. "My family is Hungarian. I was born in Hungary and ended up in Holland after the war. I always use my English as an excuse to get people to repeat themselves so I can make sure I know what they are saying, plus to decide what I am going to say. How about you? Where are you from?"

"I was born in a small town called Saluda. It is a Cherokee name and means 'field of corn.' It's just outside of Asheville, where Mr. Hudson lives."

"Yah, Asheville," the man chuckled. "The playground of the rich and famous, hey?"

"Well, I don't know about all of that," Jim said. "The only rich people I've met so far are you, Jane and Mr. Hudson."

"Well, my boy, that's more than enough to get you to almost anywhere you want to go, Lord willing."

Jim plucked his bag from the luggage cart and he and Mr. Hoffmann walked to the curbside parking area. Jim followed Hoffmann toward an unusual car parked in front of the terminal.

"Wow! This is a beauty," Jim said. "What in the world is it?"

"Well, let me tell you," Hoffman said, "as far as cars go, this is my pride and joy. And by the way, feel free to call me David?" Hoffman said as he opened the door for Jim to climb in. "My boy, you are sitting in one of the finest cars in the world. This is an Aston Martin DB4. It is one of the first three production models in the world and I was fortunate enough to get this one. It will do a top speed of 140 mph and 0-60 in about 8.5 seconds. Well, let's take her for a spin, what do you say?"

Jim had never been in a new car, let alone a high-performance European car like the one he was now sitting in, and he was amazed that it rode better than it looked. Transfixed on the lighted Chicago skyline and soothed by the whine of the finely tuned Aston Martin, Jim couldn't help but feel overwhelmed with the sense that these few short days visiting Mr. Hudson's friends would change his life forever.

At the Berghoff restaurant, David began to share with Jim while they enjoyed a fine meal.

"Jim, I am sure Jane told you our saying. Didn't she?" Hoffman began.

"Saying?" Jim asked, scratching his head.

"This little saying is at the heart of all we do. *Thoughts are things, things have gravity and gravity attracts.*"

"Oh that," he answered. "Yes, she did share that with me and also explained what it meant."

"Well, I believe that seventy percent of the reason that I am where I am today is because of that saying. The other thirty percent of that equation is what I want to talk to you about. It was almost fifteen years ago that I learned one of the most important rules in succeeding or surviving anything. What I learned is to live in a constant state of gratitude. I also learned that *until* you can live in a state of gratitude, you can never be truly wealthy."

"How do you mean, exactly?" Jim asked.

Hoffmann stopped long enough for him and Jim to order dinner and then began again. "Let me tell you a story. I grew up in Hungary and had a very happy childhood. My older brother and I started a small accounting firm in my mid-twenties. I was newly married and had just had a baby boy when the war in Europe broke out. Growing up Jewish, I always had—how do you say—a close knit family; lots of family get-togethers with brothers, aunts and uncles. When the war started, we never expected or imagined what would eventually happen. I remember it all like it was yesterday.

"It was November, I think, 1943, my brother was having dinner with my family. Just as we were finishing up the meal, Nazi SS soldiers kicked the front door open. We sat paralyzed at that moment while they stormed through the house and then rounded up my brother, my wife, and my son. They shoved my brother and me into one waiting truck and my wife and son into another. I tried desperately to reach out and touch my wife and kiss my little boy, Jake. I was able to break the grip of the guard and lunged for my wife and son. My fingertips brushed my son's warm outstretched hand as a rifle butt smashed down on my head, knocking me unconscious."

Jim had been listening intently and saw the man's eyes begin to fill with tears. But after a brief moment, Hoffman had regained his composure and continued.

"I woke up an hour or two later in a train freight car with my brother holding my bloody head in his lap. We were being shipped somewhere. Later we found out that it was a camp in Bergen-Belsen, Germany.

The camp was cold, dark and full of misery. People were sick. Unspeakable brutality and death was a daily occurrence. It must have been about February, 1944 when one day a guard started kicking an older sickly man in the stomach. I tried to stay silent but couldn't. I begged the guard to stop but he simply called me a scum Jew and struck me over the head with the butt of his rifle. I tried to get my balance as blood poured into my right eye. Soon I felt another blow to the head. Again, I stood up, now bleeding from both sides of my head. This only enraged the guard who called another to join in the beating. By then, my older brother, Seth, could not take it any more and rushed the guards, smashing one of them into a large iron post and grappling the other guard to the ground. After that, I remember hearing a gunshot and seeing my brother's body go still before I slipped into unconsciousness.

"One of the inmates, a Lutheran minister named Michael, watched over me and helped me as I regained consciousness. When the swelling went down and I was finally able to focus on him, I saw his warm loving smile and compassionate eyes that afforded me a fatigued yet calming peace. Michael cared for me until I slowly regained my health. He told me of my brother's death and comforted me as I wept. But I could find no forgiveness for myself. I blamed myself for my brother's death. If I hadn't tried to interrupt the guard, my brother would still be alive. And then the anger came and I hated."

"Oh how I hated," he said, almost whispering. He paused for a moment and then continued with his story.

"I was filled with hatred and anger at what had happened to my brother. Death was already a common occurrence in Bergen-Belsen, yet here I found myself constantly focusing on how I was going to avenge my brother's death. I hated the guards. I hated at the world. I hated God. Michael saw my hatred and anger and one day pulled me aside to share with me a secret that today I realized was one of the most valuable lessons of my life.

"What did he tell you, David?" asked Jim.

"Michael, knowing how angry and hostile I was, asked me one day was there anything that I was grateful for. 'Grateful?' I yelled at him. What do you mean, grateful? There's nothing to be grateful for. He then asked me, 'What could I be grateful for if I wanted to?' I became even more angry and yelled at him to open his eyes and look around. We're in a death camp, people are being murdered, my brother was killed trying to save me, and for what? There is nothing to be grateful for. We are prisoners of these satanic animals and God does nothing. Absolutely nothing! I don't even think there is a God."

"David," he then said, "I see how angry you are and, yes, it true that we are in the middle of death and suffering, but is there anything you could be grateful for if you chose to be grateful? Learning to live in the spirit of gratitude is the ultimate control over life. But, living in gratitude means surrendering to a higher purpose for our lives. Yes, we are in captivity, suffering under the hands of ruthless madmen, but the ability to control what we think and feel is the only thing they cannot control. If we have faith that somehow everything that we are going through right now is shaping and molding us for our ultimate purpose, we can have access to all that we are capable of creating and receiving."

Hoffman went on to tell Jim how Michael had begun to share many passages of scripture from both the Torah and the Bible that stated that what we thought about most and backed with feeling in our heart is what and who we became. Faith in bad thoughts begets bad. Faith in good thoughts begets good. Faith in great thoughts begets greatness.

"Speaking of thoughts and faith let me take just a second to tell you about a funny thing happened to me yesterday," Hoffman said. "A friend of mine introduced me to this older fellow yesterday that pretty much shows what I am talking about regarding thinking and faith. Anyway, this fellow is around 70 years old and totally committed to a fried chicken recipe he has developed. He believes he will get restaurants all around the nation to use his recipe to sell more chicken and they will give him a nickel for each chicken they sell using his recipe. I figured I would try to introduce him to Chester Brown who you are meeting next, but the unique thing about this man was his absolute faith in what he was doing and that strange white suit he wore. I don't know how, but with faith like that, he should be successful. It also sounded like he had the discipline to stay focused as he must have had some sort of a military background because my friend kept referring to him as the Colonel. Anyway, let me get back to the story— I just thought that was something interesting that emphasized my point," David said with a smile.

"Michael told me that the mark of a man who would ultimately fulfill his God-given purpose in life was a man who could constantly live in trust," Hoffman said. "He explained that when we prayed we had to be grateful to God for giving us that which we prayed for as if we already had it. He explained that most men and women were grateful only when something good happened in their lives and missed being grateful for the very challenges that ultimately make them great. He explained that if I let the sacrifice of my brother's life create or spawn hatred and anger in my heart, then the Nazi regime would ultimately win not only my brother's life, but also my own. He said that if I was grateful for nothing more than the opportunity to share the story with future generations of my people, to share the story of my brother's courage and ultimate sacrifice, it would be worth it. He said you could bury my brother's body, but his character would never be buried. My brother's life would continue forever through me and the others he touched. And his sacrifice would help ensure that this never happened again.

"Mr. Hoffman.…..David, I'm not sure I understand what you are saying," Jim said. "Was Michael telling you that you shouldn't be angry over your brother's murder?"

"Jim, what he was really saying is that anger is a destructive thought which only takes away from my life. It opens me up for deception and loss of control, whereas gratitude is a constructive emotion which can cause me to tap into what is possible. Gratitude is related to trust, and it is trust that strengthens me through gratitude."

"For example, I once heard a story of two farmers, a father and son. They were taking their produce to the market. The boy was anxious to get there so they could get the best location and highest profits. The father however took his time visiting relatives and taking scenic paths effectively costing them a whole day. The son was now livid. With a whole day lost, their wagon slowly winded toward the city when they heard an awful noise that sounded like thunder. They looked into the sky but there were no thunder clouds, only a curious cloud far ahead in the distance. As they crested the ridge on the familiar mountain path, they looked with shock down in the valley where the bustling city market of Nagasaki, once stood," David continued. "You see Jim the boy was very angry with his dad for his apparent delay. He could have chosen to be grateful for his father and trust that God's hand was on the trip, rather he allowed himself to be engulfed with anger toward his Dad. However, as the story illustrates our plans are not always what is best for us. Wherever we find ourselves, we must be grateful and trust."

"Trust in what? God?" asked Jim.

"Exactly," David answered. "What I learned from Michael is that if you are going to achieve anything in life, it begins with gratitude. You have to be grateful for both the good and bad because through the lens of gratitude there is only good—Divinely designed good. Your gratitude must become a habit rather than an event. Let me give you an example, have you ever done great on a school test and thanked God for your good grade?"

"Yes, I think so," said Jim.

"Imagine, if instead of just being grateful for your good grade, you were constantly grateful for your intelligence, your ability to learn, your incredible ability to focus. Even more, what if you were grateful for the fact that you live in a country where you are allowed to attend school, grateful for the fact you didn't have to pay to go to school, and could go to the library to have access to most any book you wanted for free? Imagine how living in a spirit of gratitude like this might change the way you think about life."

"But your brother, your wife, your baby boy…" Jim questioned. "How could you possibly be grateful?

"Trust," David said. "It is the hardest lesson of all. Trusting can hurt, but if you just remember that everything is God's to begin with and that we are only managers, or stewards, of His things while here on earth."

"Yes, I'm starting to understand," Jim said. "But can people really think like that?"

David warmly smiled at Jim. "Yes, son, especially those people who end up extremely wealthy. And when I say wealth, I am not speaking only of money, but the blessings that are so much more valuable such as family, love, and legacy. Well my boy, we've had a great meal, and I know it will be a busy day come tomorrow. What do you say I take you back to the Hilton, get you checked in and will take up our talk in the morning? What do you say I send a car over to pick you up in morning at 7:00am? We'll take breakfast in my office," he said, standing up.

"Thanks again, David, and I am grateful for the ride to the hotel. Can I ask one more question? What happened to your family?"

"Well Jim, remember how I said 'trust'?"

"Yes."

"Over time Michael helped convince me, and my heart changed," Hoffman explained. "I trusted God every day until I had absolutely no doubt. As hard as it may seem, I was even able to live daily in gratitude while in that terrible place. I asked God to forgive the guards that killed my brother. I found a little blessing in the Bible in I Chronicles 4:9-10 and I asked this blessing daily over myself and everyone and everything I cared about. When we were finally liberated, I was one of the few fortunate survivors. I immediately did everything I could to find my wife and my baby boy. My trust strengthened me daily; however, as each day of searching went by, I gradually began to believe that somehow maybe it was God's will that I not be reunited with my family. My hurt was deep, greater than I had ever known. And as I was just about to accept that somehow their lives were lost, I met a woman who had seemingly met my wife and son only six months earlier. She had been sent to a medical camp where my wife served as a nurse, and our boy was with her. When I learned that the camp was just outside of Hannover twenty miles away, my heart leapt for joy. I ran toward the city, and when I couldn't run, I walked. All night, I pushed until I could barely go on, even though I was weak from malnutrition and exhaustion. As dawn approached, I looked up to see a line of hundreds of people leaving the camp. Hungry and exhausted, I hobbled down the hill hoping to find someone who knew my wife. I trusted God to help me and I wept in hope as I ran. I came to the front of the line and struggled over to a woman at the head of the group hoping I could learn something about the whereabouts of my family. With her back to me, I let out a faint cry for help. She must not have heard, so I tried again, even louder, for her to please help me. Still as if she had heard nothing, she bent down, picked up her child and turned to toward me. Perhaps time stopped, for when I saw those familiar loving blue eyes, my own wife's precious eyes, I cried out to God with thanksgiving. So I tell you, Jim, trust, just trust!

Seven in the morning came quickly for Jim. He showered, dressed and met Mr. Hoffman's car and driver in front of the Hilton. They reached David's office in less than five minutes where they greeted each other and sat down to an array of breads, fresh fruit and eggs.

"Did you sleep well, Jim?" asked David.

"I sure did—like a log, we would say back home," he said. "But I have to tell you, I couldn't stop thinking about the story you told me yesterday. I can't imagine how you survived all of that."

"One day at a time. Jim, becoming who God needs you to become isn't always easy, but as you grow in your understanding of Him, you will discover what seems to be the hard way is ultimately the easy way. I believe there is a purpose to all things including our lives and what we do with them. Do you remember yesterday when we talked about how the wealthy think, how the ones that do not appreciate what they have achieved seem to lose it?"

"I remember it well, David."

"Well, interestingly enough," Hoffman continued, "many of the wealthy have stumbled on to this fact by accident. But some of the wiser families who have been wealthy for generations, teach this to each of their generations. And if it is ever forgotten and not taught to the next generation, their wealth quickly disappears. Yes, sir, knowing exactly what it is you want, while at the same time being grateful for the situations and circumstances in which you find yourself. While you resolve yourself to pay the price for what you want, are three of the best kept secrets of the *truly* wealthy."

"Let me see if I have understood what you are saying," Jim said. "You mean that if I get crystal clear about what I want and stay grateful through the process of getting it, regardless of what happens to me, then I can become *truly* wealthy?"

"Yes, in a nutshell, as you Americans say, I think you have it, Lord willing! Just remember the butterfly."

"The butterfly?" Jim asked with a puzzled look.

"The butterfly," Hoffman said. "The butterfly starts out as a caterpillar and spins a cocoon around itself. As the caterpillar is transformed into a butterfly, its increasing size begins to push against the cocoon. The cocoon vibrates and stretches. The cocoon moves back and forth as the emerging butterfly grows. Eventually after many weeks the butterfly has struggled against that cocoon and grown to the point that a tip of its wing punches through. The tip pushes further and further through the cocoon until eventually becoming a whole wing. After a short while, the rest of the body bursts through the cocoon, revealing a magnificent butterfly. What's interesting about this story, Jim, is that if you attempt to help the butterfly break through its cocoon early by gently scoring the side of the cocoon lightly with a pen knife, you are dooming the butterfly to a life without flight. It is the delay, and struggle against the cocoon, that makes the butterfly strong enough to break through the cocoon. The cocoon is spun according to a divine formula for each specific butterfly. It isn't too strong or the butterfly would never break through and eventually starve to death. It's not too weak or the butterfly would not have struggled sufficiently to gain the strength to fly. It's made perfectly. It is this same perfection that gives us the perfectly designed struggle so we can one day fly, nothing more, nothing less. The key is gratitude and the ability to embrace the struggle."

"If I understand correctly," Jim said, "it is our growth and struggle that makes us strong enough to fly. So the butterfly should be grateful for the struggle, since it would never otherwise be able to fly and would be eaten by whatever came along."

Hoffman nodded. "The more you remain in the spirit of gratitude, the quicker the wealth you seek will be attracted to you. And when it seems as though it is not happening quickly enough, remain in the spirit of gratitude because God's delays are not God's denials. Remember the story of the farmers being delayed to market in Nagasaki. The bottom line is making "Gratitude" equal to "Godattitude."

"Godatttitude?" Jim asked with a big smile. "Now I know you're going to tell me about that."

"Godattitude is what I call the "wealth attitude" that places explicit trust in God. This is a simple idea to talk about but it can take a lifetime to practice," Hoffman explained. "When somebody tells me they trust in God, I ask them why they are worried." Now you know the second secret of wealth…stay in gratitude by trusting God.

"Okay, David," Jim said. "If you don't mind, I'd like to go over what you've taught me today."

"That would be fine my boy," said David.

"Well, here's what I've learned from you," said Jim.

Jim's Notes

- Thoughts are things, things have gravity, and gravity attracts. What are your thoughts attracting into your life?

- It's important to develop the habit of gratitude in *all* things!

- Being grateful keeps me mindful of what I have, not what I don't have.

- Being grateful reminds me that there is always an opportunity to learn from whatever happens to me.

- Be grateful for the things I am striving for as though, in fact, they are being attracted to me at this very moment.

- Remember the butterfly and welcome the struggle of growth because when I'm big enough, I will break through the "success cocoon."

- God's delays are not God's denials.

- Stop worrying and trust in God

"Well done, my boy," Hoffman responded. "Just remember that you become what you think about most. You must stay in the spirit of Godattitude while you are reaching your goals or you may give up and never reach them, and this is the key: you must never, never, give up, but continue trusting that where you are at any given moment is God's choice for your own growth and strength. That is what Godattitude is all about. Don't focus so much on what feels good for the moment; rather focus on what makes you great in the end. From my story, you now know strength of character is not built with sunshine and flowers; rather we reach the sunshine and flowers after we struggle out of our cocoon. Gratitude, my boy—gratitude is strength that allows us to fly."

"David, I want to tell you how much I appreciate your sharing time with me," said Jim.

"I, too, enjoyed the time," Hoffman answered. "I just want to let you know that I am proud of you. Stop and think about how many young people may never learn this. You are so far ahead of the game, my boy. It is my hope that you may teach a few others some of the many things Mr. Hudson has taught us."

Jim smiled, looked at his watch and told David that he needed to get going to catch his next flight.

"You're going to see Chester in Dallas, aren't you?" Hoffman asked. "Well, you tell old 'Flash' that Davy said hello. You won't meet a more loving and considerate fellow. Talk about gratitude, I think if there is anyone who lives with pure Godattitude, he is it. He built a whole chain of chicken restaurants and donated over thirty percent of his profits to helping those in need. And when you want something done, just leave it up to Flash. As he always says, 'I don't grow no moss.' He is one who gets the job done with no procrastination on his part. And so we part, my boy. Have a great trip."

On the plane, Jim considered how fortunate he was to have had the opportunity to meet such people as David and Jane. He closed his eyes and silently thanked God for all the blessings of the last two days. He nodded off to sleep still thinking about David's incredible story. He awoke a few hours later to see the city lights of Dallas as they approached for landing.

The Wealth Of Action

"You may not always be able to control what happens to you, but you can control how you respond."

Jon Bender

Jim sleepily climbed the stairs of the boarding bridge into the terminal and wondered how he would know Chester Brown. Perhaps Mr. Hudson had described what he looked like to Mr. Brown. Entering the terminal, he scanned all the people to look for anyone who looked like they might be looking for him. He didn't see anybody so he decided to head down to the baggage area. A big hand gently grabbed his shoulder and he cautiously turned to find a kindly old black man dressed in a navy blue suit staring down at him.

"Are you Jim?" asked the old man.

"Yes, sir, I am," said Jim.

"Well, young man, I am here to pick you up," the man said, taking Jim's shoulders in his two big hands.

"Great," said Jim. "Did Mr. Brown send you?"

"Well, I guess you could say that," he said, smiling and extending his right hand. "I am Mr. Brown, Chester Brown, and glad to meet you, Jim. Shall we go get your luggage?" asked Chester.

"Yes, sir" said Jim, trying to hide his embarrassment.

Jim had assumed that the gentleman he met was Mr. Brown's driver and not Mr. Brown. He had seen only a few black men in his lifetime. His hometown of Saluda had only one black family and the people in the town treated that family with the same disdain that they treated him and his mother.

Chester Brown, seeming unnerved by Jim's assumption, collected the baggage and carried it out the door. Awaiting curbside was another beautiful stretch limousine. This one looked even nicer than Jane's. Mr. Brown's driver, Gregory, a twenty-something light-skinned and handsome young college student, immediately got out of the limousine and took the bag from Mr. Brown. Chester introduced the two and told Gregory that Jim would be staying the night out at his house.

"Mr. Brown," Jim stammered. "I have to admit that I have never seen such a big, beautiful car. I thought Jane's car was big, but yours is even bigger,"

"Jim, please call me Chester," Brown said. "And I must admit I think it is big and beautiful, too. Thank you for those kind words. Not too shabby for an old man who didn't get his first car until he was fifty years old. What about you, will you be driving soon?" he asked Jim.

"I hope so, but I think I'll probably be like you and not be able to get my first real car until I'm also fifty," Jim replied catching himself jokingly being negative.

"Well, young man, you may find some of the things Jane, David and I teach you will rub off and allow you to get that car a little sooner," he said through a laugh. "But if you want to wait until you are 50, it's up to you…remember, thoughts are things, things have gravity…"

"And gravity attracts," Jim interrupted. "What are your thoughts attracting into your life?" Jim said finishing the mantra.

"Good," said Chester. "I see you are well on your way."

For the next twenty minutes, Chester and Jim spent the time talking about Saluda and North Carolina. Chester told Jim that his father and grandfather were all from the New Bern area of North Carolina. Jim admitted to Chester that he had not had the chance to meet many black folks. Chester laughed and told him when he was Jim's age, he hadn't met many white folks either.

The limousine pulled off the highway onto a beautifully paved driveway. On either side of the driveway there were what appeared to be green pastures. The glow of the headlights cast a spotlight on the boxwoods that flanked either side of the drive-way. Jim's view was blocked to the front, but what after seemed to be half a mile, the limo slowly began to round a circle to reveal a beautifully lit mansion. Chester called it his ranch and though Jim didn't know exactly what that meant, he did know that he had only seen one mansion bigger—Mr. Hudson's.

Jim stepped out of the limo, and taking in the view before him, he noticed how the huge limousine looked dwarfed by the enormous mansion. Outdoor architectural lighting cast a warm glow on the mansion's ornate masonry and woodwork. He felt the excitement building and realized how eager he was to hear the story of Chester Brown's success.

Chester led him into the grand foyer of the house and began telling Jim how fortunate he was to have met Mr. Hudson at such an early age. "I was forty-seven when I met him," Brown told him. "And I tell you, you can't imagine what twenty years can do. Or, maybe you can because you're standing in the middle of it."

Jim admired the home, noticing the checkered marble floor with the two grand curved staircases flanking either side of the foyer.

"Ah, but I bet you are tired and ready for bed," Chester said noticing the dazed look in Jim's eyes.

"Actually, Mr. Brown...."

"Uh, uh, uh," Jim was interrupted by Chester. "Please call me Chester. If we are going to be friends, it's got to be on a first-name basis," he said.

"Well, what I mean, Chester, is I actually slept on the plane and I'm really not too tired at all," said Jim.

"Well, in that case, we'll go to the library and get started with some of the things you are here to learn." Chester led Jim into a large

5545564

4564555445444

oak library with beautiful bookcases—filled with books of every size and color—that traced out the circumference of the room.

Mr. Brown listened intently as young Jim shared his story. He told Mr. Brown about his loving mother and how he had come to know Mr. Hudson. Mr. Brown was impressed by the courage, determination and persistence of this young man to get an audience with Mr. Hudson in such a creative manner.

"Jim, I'm going to tell you that becoming wealthy and staying wealthy never comes by accident. Whether a person knows it or not, they are doing things in a certain way to get the results that they are getting," said Chester.

Chester explained that when he was young he experienced things that a young person should not ever have to see. He told Jim about the terrible racism and violence he had witnessed within his own family and friends. He shared how he had seen the systematic discrimination and degradation of his people. Yet through all of this he kept on, determined to make a better life for himself. He explained to Jim that when he was growing up, he had hope for the future and lived each day with the notion that there was power in each and every day as long as he was willing to learn and seek ways to love people. Chester believed that every day was worth living.

And if it was worth living it was worth living it to its fullest doing the best you can along the way.

"I remember when I was forty-seven Mr. Hudson gave me a book on Abraham Lincoln. This book had something special in it – a kind of secret if you will," said Chester.

"What kind of secret?" asked Jim.

"Well it was a secret that, combined with what Mr. Hudson has taught me, has helped me build the number of successful restaurants that we have today," he said. Chester told Jim that in that book was a small adage that supposedly President Lincoln's mother used to tell him every day while he was growing up. "It's a saying that I figure made me my first million. It goes like this, 'Whether a job big or small, do it right or not at all, once a job has be...' "

Jim joined in and recited with Chester in unison, "...begun, see it through until it's done."

"You are not going to believe it, but Mrs. Thompson back home must have told me that little poem more than a thousand times," Jim said. "Now I know where she got it."

"Well, that explains it," said Chester. "No wonder you had the persistence to find a way to contact Robert"

"Wow, I had no idea where that came from," Jim said with a smile.

"I have no doubt that Mr. Hudson told you his favorite quote from his old Scottish friend and mentor Andrew Carnegie about persistence. Do you remember?" asked Chester.

"Yes, sir, I do," said Jim. "Carbon is to steel as persistence is to the character of mankind."

"Jim, persistence is important, but persistence also has a twin brother called action. Together 'persistent action' is the real secret. Persistent action is like the wind that pushes a sailing ship. The best rudder on the best sailboat is useless without wind. Just as wind fills a sail, you must back what you desire with persistent action toward it. With persistence, even drops of water can wear a hole through stone and yes, even steel. Everything that Mr. Hudson, Jane, David or I have taught you so far will amount to nothing without being put into action persistently."

"I think I already know, but to be sure, tell me what the best way to develop persistence is?" Jim asked.

"It begins with a decision. You must resolve yourself to do all you can do every day regardless of what the people around you say. Anybody can get excited about something for a while, but it's the time after the "for a while" part that is the key to persistent action toward success. A person who can't inspire themselves to taking persistent action is destined for mediocrity or worse. I figure it is like this. Folks pretty much get what they absolutely must have, nothing more, nothing less. Since most folks are okay with existing at a state lower than their God-given potential, then that is pretty much what they get, something less than what God had intended for them or, as I said, mediocrity. Remember, God gives us freedom of choice. I have met two kinds of people in the world. The first is the kind of person that knows that there is something more out there for them and chooses to take persistent action to get it. The second is the kind of person who pretty much sits and waits and chooses to settle with what the world gives them.

"The primary difference between the two groups is the first group has a sense of purpose and chooses to fight to see that purpose fulfilled by using persistence and action. Persistent action means you pull out all the stops and really do all you can do every hour that you work. This doesn't mean you work all the time. It does mean that when you work, you work smart with persistent action. A person taking persistent action toward a clear objective is kind of like the sailboat example earlier. They point their boat toward a lighthouse on shore. No matter how rough the waves are, they use their rudder to keep their boat pointed toward the lighthouse with their sail cloth full of wind. They may get knocked off course, or they may have to tack against the wind, but they return to that course and keep sailing toward the light with the wind at their back. Eventually, no matter how big the waves or how strong the currents, if they persist, they'll make it to the shore.

Jim, as you go through life, keep thinking about the sailboat. Remember the lighthouse is your purpose driven goal; your ability to think about and focus on the lighthouse continuously becomes your rudder. The sail is the plan of action and the wind is the persistent action behind your plan. The waves, currents and storms are all the things in life that get in the way of your getting to the lighthouse or as our buddy, Davey Hoffman says, they're part of the cocoon you are going to have to break through.

"Now let me tell you about the second group. The second group has a boat, too. Yet in their perception of life, there is no shore. There is no light. And if by chance they get inspired to row, they will row for some time but they will stop shortly thereafter thinking what's the point—no sails, no wind, no rowing, no rudder, just a boat adrift in the sea of life. This is how many people live their lives. So it all comes down to this, once you know where you are going and why you are going there, move forward without hesitation. Focus and move forward with everything you've got. The stronger the movement forward, the greater the results. I have always made a point that once I start something, I will go with it full blast until it is done, if you know what I mean."

"Is that why David calls you 'Flash'?" Jim asked.

"Ole' Davey knows me well," Chester smiled. "Yep, they call me 'Flash' because I do things now, this moment...even if my initial plan is not perfect. I don't wait. I can always tweak it as I go. I don't put off until some other time. I get it done in a flash and as I always say, 'There ain't no moss that is going to grow under ole' Chester's feet. I get things done in a flash!"

He continued with his story to Jim.

"My grandfather who came up in slavery times used to say it like this, 'Boy, get that freedom in your heart no matter how life whoops you. Every day, and I mean every day, do all you can do and you'll be free as a bird, boy, free as a bird!'"

Jim thought he saw some sentimental pride when Chester recited his grandfather's words.

"Your grandfather sounded like a smart man," said Jim.

"No Jim he was the *wisest* man I ever met and he never had a lick of school. He was wise in the ways of the world, but also knew what was pleasing to God and those ways are what he taught me. You see, Jim, everything is a choice. You may think you're in control, but the only thing I know for sure is that we can control how we respond to situations. You may not always be able to control what happens to you, but you can control how you respond. This is the secret I want to share with you. *Win with the cards you've been dealt.* Sure, that is easier said than done, but nevertheless it can be done and this philosophy has and continues to be the seed of the greatest victories. Look at that fellow Gandhi over in India. He played his hand well and liberated a nation without raising a finger in violence.

"Let me tell you about a story that starts when I was a boy. I came up in the time when it was much worse for the black man than it is today. I used to wonder why white folks could say and do what they did to us. When we went to town, if my momma didn't step aside on the sidewalk when a white lady walked by, she was likely to get spit on. I tell you, Jimmy, it used to make me boiling mad, but then I realized anger and hate turned me into exactly what I disliked most in those folks that I hated. And then it hit me one day while reading my Bible, it's a lot harder to love than to hate. I also realized it took a stronger man to love his enemy than to fight that enemy.

104

So I made a choice: I would not let negativity and hatred enter my thoughts or possess me. I wouldn't let old Lucifer get his hooks in me; rather, I constantly encouraged and moved people forward with kindness, black or white, anytime and every time I could. I figured if I was positive and praised folks long enough, no matter how tough things got, sooner or later I could create the world around me that I wanted for me and my family. After a while, white and black folks alike knew me as one who always found the good in people and situations as well as one that got the job done...in a *flash*!

"Jim, I've been alive nearly seventy years and if I just walk down the street today in downtown Dallas, it's not but just a few minutes before I hear, 'boy', 'negro' or just plain 'nigger.' I feel sorry for these folks and look at their bigotry and ignorance as gifts that I can learn from. You see, I have chosen to observe and feel the fear in these folks rather than believe that I have to accept and internalize their ridicule as meaningful. I don't know what it is like being them, but what I do know is that someone isn't born that way; they learn to hate. I remember when I was a boy about seven years old. I was playing with the little white boy down the road and his daddy caught him playing kickball with me. He whipped him with a chain he found in the back of his pickup truck just because he was playing with me. I loved my friend, but even he, given time and training, started calling me a nigger a few months after that. Ever since that day, I have always remembered that hate doesn't just happen, it is man-made and not of God. My old granny used to say it best: 'Hate the sin; not the sinner.' Jim, I won't try to kid you, it's been real hard at times, but that's what I have done over the years. And a big part of my success has been persistent action. You can't let the waves or currents get you, they will come and go, they will knock you off course and delay your success, but you just got to keep sailing toward the shore focused on the light.

"You know, every society has its prejudices and beliefs. It has always been this way. Most of these change over time, but if you are going to succeed you must work within the society you live in while never selling out your beliefs and integrity. Here's an example: I employ several thousand people and serve millions of people a year at my restaurants. Yet, very few people know that these restaurants are owned by a "colored man." I realized when I was building each of my restaurants that very few people believed a black man could be successful at any business. But rather than fight their ignorance as if I needed to prove something, I chose to love them by being totally focused and committed to my dream of giving the best food possible to *all* men and women regardless of race. It was my destiny, I believe. Throughout that time, I was ridiculed and scorned, I was beaten and stolen from, but I continued to love and be positive. I refused to give up and kept on keeping on. And today, by the grace of God, I am able to serve millions of people, not as a "lucky" black man who has done well, but as a "blessed" man who stayed the course and loved and uplifted people wherever he went. In a nutshell, Jim, here's the secret: use persistent action. I mean hit it hard giving all that you have to give on the days or hours that you work and always at the service of people, giving more than you receive. Now here is the tricky part. Remember, you are not doing all this to make yourself feel more important or famous; you are doing these things to support and encourage other people to feel important. And last but not least, work within the conditions that you find yourself. Never sell out, and along the way, keep your integrity intact!

"A Chinese proverb says 'the reason the mountain praises the stream is because the stream always stays beneath the mountain. Yet the power of the stream is the only thing that cuts and shapes the mountain.' You see, I always regarded myself as the stream. It's interesting now, looking back, that the greatest gift in doing this for all those years was not in what I have today in material things, rather it is the genuine respect and admiration that I receive from so many people."

"Wow, I have never heard anyone talk like you," said Jim. "You should write this down."

"Well, I guess you could say I am writing it down. I am writing it down in you, Jim. You're a young man who knows that there is something greater in store for you. You are also willing to fight for it," said Chester.

"Thanks, Chester, but I don't know," Jim said. "I don't really know if I could ever be able to share the kind of things you have shared with me. You just seem so much stronger than me."

"How do you mean, exactly?" Chester asked.

"Well, I come from a real simple place," Jim answered. "We have simple thoughts. I mean, I am just an ordinary person. I got picked on and ridiculed my whole life. I got beat up and knocked down by almost everyone. I mean, I know God loves me, but sometimes I just have a hard time imagining that I could grow up to be important and teach people anything...like you have taught me."

"Jim, I know just what you mean," Chester said. "In fact, I felt that way for almost forty-seven years until Robert taught me something. And I am going to share that with you right now. You see, we tend to doubt ourselves because of things that happened to us when we were young children. Just like I told you, I grew up in a time when a black child saw all kinds of things that caused him to feel inferior and just plain worthless. Remember when I told you how my little white friend's daddy whipped him just for playing with me because I was black? Well, Jim, that really hurt me. No, it traumatized and scarred me as a child to think that someone I loved was brutalized because of the color of *my* skin. Mr. Hudson taught me how to go in and erase the scar and to release myself from self limiting thoughts that were anchored in my emotions forty years earlier. It is a concept he calls 'Forward Scaping'."

"Forward Scaping," Jim asked. "What is it?"

"Well you know what Forward means. And 'Scape' comes from an English word which means *vista* or a *distant view.*"

"You see, Jim, I felt that God could do something significant with me. I wanted to heal and get beyond the trauma of the past. I learned that Forward Scaping is a way to release emotional scars through loving yourself. It is also used for creating a magnetically charged future and thus the name Forward Scaping. Let me give you an illustration of how it worked for me. I would close my eyes, go back, and remember in vivid detail and emotion that horrible moment when I watched my little friend being whipped. I was crying as they drove away in his daddy's pickup truck. As I remembered this horrible moment, I would imagine transporting myself back in time, as a full-grown man to standing right behind the child version of myself. Let's call him little Chester. Little Chester was still crying at that very moment. And then I'd tap little Chester on the shoulder. As he turned around, he would be startled by my appearing from nowhere standing right in front of him. I would smile and tell him not to be afraid. I would kneel down in front of him and the boy would sense that I was no danger to him. He would ask, 'Who are you?' in his small child's voice. Then I would lovingly smile and gently taking his hand in mine, I'd say, 'I am you. I am from the future. I want you to know how much I love you. I see that you are hurting and sad. I want you to know I love you, Little Chester, and it is going to be okay. What just happened isn't your fault. You are precious to me.' I then wipe the tears from his little cheeks and pull him closer to embrace him in an accepting and loving hug. As I hugged him I'd tell him, 'I know you are hurting, but I want you to be strong. We have such a powerful future ahead of us and you must hang in there. Remember, what happened to your friend is not your fault. I know how bad it hurts you, but it is not your fault. You are important, God loves you so much and we have a wonderful future together.' I would then remind him that without him, there is no "us" in the future. I would hug him once again, telling him I loved him and then I would bring myself back to the present moment. I would do this nightly over and over again for every scarring moment that I could remember from my childhood. After a short time, I began to notice that, as an adult, I was feeling much better about who I was and what I was capable of doing. It was like anchors being cut away from a boat that had been stuck for decades. After a while, I began to feel free of the old limitations or anchors and, as you can see, the rest is history. I began to grow in success!

"I can understand that, but why do you call it forward if you use it to heal your past," asked Jim.

"Jim that is a fantastic question. Remember how I said it was like having anchors cut away from a stuck ship? Well the first step is to fix the past so you can move forward. Then you can use the "forward" part of Forward Scaping to create a compelling future. When Robert first shared this with me, I was forty-seven. He told me that after I was free from my past limitations, I could go into the future and create an unstoppable future 'self'." So I imagined myself in the future when I would be seventy-two years old. I imagined in vivid detail and with great emotion who I was, what I had accomplished, and the man I had become. Each night, I would lie in bed and imagine that that seventy-two-year-old self would come back to the present and visit my present forty-seven year old self. My future self would tap me on the shoulder and would share the glorious future in store for us. My future self would remind me that where I was in life right now was part of the process and would encourage me to keep on working with fearless persistent action. My future self would hug my present self, remind me to trust God and give me an affirming slap on the back and then disappear into the future.

"Good Lord, Jimmy, I did that so many nights while lying in bed that it became so real it was as if I was flying off to the future. It was as if my future self had come back and hooked a giant rubber band to me that would pull me into the future with total certainty. Today that certainty has become my reality!

You can use this Forward Scaping to free yourself from any past destructive anchors and experiences and to create an incredible future to ultimately become whoever God has purposed you to become."

"Wow ...," Jim just kept repeating himself like a broken record. He was still overwhelmed with the idea Chester had put before him and at the same time had a strange feeling that his life would be forever transformed from what he had just heard. Chester told Jim there was much more to tell and learn, but he would leave it for the morning.

It was a beautiful morning after a fitful night of sleep. He had so many ideas racing through his mind and he couldn't help but dream of how all that he was learning would affect him for the rest of his life. He only wished his mother could be here to hear all the great things he had learned. Would he be able to explain it to anyone else, he wondered?

Chester met Jim for breakfast on a beautiful stone veranda overlooking a tranquil pond. The sun had just risen, leaving a beautiful mist over the water. "Did you sleep well, Jim?" asked Chester.

"To be honest with you, I couldn't sleep. I just kept thinking about what you said and what I have learned. There are so many ideas running through my head that I can't stop my mind from racing," Jim said.

"That's okay; you are trying to get a lifetime of realization into just a few short days. I don't expect I would get much sleep, either, if I were you and especially at your age," Chester said. "I wanted to share one more thing with you before we take you to the airport this afternoon. I don't know if you believe in God, but I want to tell you something. God believes in you. Each one of us has a purpose and our mission in life is to find that purpose and to have the courage to follow it."

Chester explained to Jim how he would feel at peace when he perceived that he was doing God's will and would not feel that peace if he wasn't. Jim asked him about what "peace" felt like. Chester simply smiled and said that he would know when it happened.

"Jim," Chester said, "you must never accept what the world calls failure. Failure doesn't exist. Only the thought of failure exists if you allow it. David explained 'struggle' to you, no doubt. Failure is struggle that quits. Victory is struggle that doesn't. It's that simple. Remember, Jim, embrace struggle, grow, and let God build you up victoriously. Failure doesn't exist, only struggle and victories. Choose to persist through the struggle to victory. Always keep that in mind, especially when you feel as though you are persisting and things just don't seem to work out as you have planned. Sometimes we think a delay in our own plans is a denial by God and a failure, but of course God knows better and always delivers a better plan and victory in the appropriate time."

"Chester, I can't believe how much you have shared with me. David was right when he told me how amazing you are. If it is okay with you please let me read back to you what I have written down in my notes to make sure I have it correct."

Jim's Notes:

- Win with the hand you are dealt.

- Be a chronic good-finder.

- Hate the sin; not the sinner.

- Keep your integrity and convictions, but operate within the boundaries and circumstances you find yourself.

- Everyday you decide to work, do *all* you can do to work toward your desires.

- Use Forward Scaping to break away anchors that may be holding you back.

- Use Forward Scaping to create a compelling future that is consistent with God's will for you.

- Failure is struggle that quits. Victory is struggle that does not quit.

- Be okay with God's timing in your victories; do not emotionally invest in your own timing.

"Well, Jim," Chester said, "I would have to say that I couldn't have said it better myself." Chester smiled at Jim handing him an envelope and telling him that Mr. Hudson had asked that Chester deliver it to him. "Well, look at the clock, my boy," he said. "I would say we have just about enough time to get you to the airport."

Chester and Jim headed to the airport in the same limousine that they had arrived in. Chester insisted that Jim take a moment and open up the sealed envelope given to him by Mr. Hudson. Jim turned the envelope over and recognized the wax seal as being the same seal engraved in the granite threshold of Mr. Hudson's front door. Jim opened the letter and read:

Dear Jim:

By now I hope you are beginning to understand the true nature of wealth. Wealth is elusive to most because it is so much more than money. As you now know, wealth is a mindset of clarity. Wealth is a mindset of gratitude. Wealth is a mindset of action. Wealth is a mindset of persistence. Wealth is a mindset embracing the struggle. Wealth is all these things, yet wealth ultimately comes down to one more truth that without all the above statements has little or no meaning. The truth is in our lives almost every day, yet many never see it. You have heard it no doubt many times over the last few days. It is a crucible where all other wealth characteristics are synergistically combined.

When you get back to Asheville, my car will pick you up and I will bring you back to my house and share this truth with you.

Jim, you are well on your way and once I share this truth with you it will become impossible for you to fail.

Have a safe trip and I will see you in a few hours.

Best of Success,

Robert Hudson

Jim smiled as he folded the letter and slipped it back in the envelope. He sat silent for just a moment and found himself struggling with the realization that he was learning secrets from people that were multi-millionaires, secrets that would someday prove to change his life and the lives of his children's children forever.

"Chester, do you know what the last truth to wealth is?" asked Jim.

"Yes, and without it I would have nothing." Chester said. "I've already mentioned it to you at least twice today. In fact, it is something that is so obvious it can be easy to miss. However, you will soon learn that this truth will set you free. It is the easiest thing to do while at the same time, it is the hardest, and yet can be reduced to a simple question."

"You won't give me another hint, will you?" said Jim.

"I just did," Chester smiled.

Ultimate Wealth

"Trust By Pleasing God; Please By Trusting God"

Jon Bender

Jim knocked on the ornately carved oak door and entered Mr. Hudson's library.

"Jim! Great to see you, my boy," Mr. Hudson said, standing up behind his huge desk with his hands out-stretched. Robert greeted the young man with a hearty hand shake and a hug.

"I am glad to be back, Mr. Hudson!"

"Have a seat," he said, motioning for Jim to take a chair. "How was your trip?"

"It was so amazing, I can't believe everything I learned," Jim said.

"Knowing how to think and believe is the first step to real wealth," said Robert "Thinking and believing what you know is the real task. So, I know you must be tired, but if you will take just a few minutes and tell me what you learned, I would like give you the final secret I mentioned in the letter. It is not readily known, but once I share it with you, it will unlock everything you have learned so that you can use it to its maximum potential."

"I can't wait," Jim said. "My head is buzzing with so much that I have learned, but I have been waiting all day to learn this last truth so here is what I've already learned," he said. "I learned that thoughts are things, things have gravity and gravity attracts. I learned that what we think about most is the very thing that we attract into our life. I learned that what we attract and how fast it comes is in direct proportion to the clarity of what we think about. I learned that we have to be careful because we will get what we focus on, good or bad. So we have to seek God's will for us and look for what our purpose is. I also learned that if our success is to take root and last a long time, we must remember to help others by giving more than we receive. Success starts with gratitude and gratitude starts with trusting God and struggle is to be embraced. Rather than strive for what feels good, focus on what makes us great. I learned that we must yield to God's purpose and develop a Godattitude in all things. And that you have to work within the situation you are given whether it is fair or is not fair; instead, succeed despite your circumstances. I learned that this is done by doing all you can do everyday regardless of what or how many times you may feel like you get knocked down. I learned a rudder only works with motion. I learned that failure does not really exist except for those that ultimately give up and quit. Failure doesn't really exist and if believe in failure, it can keep us from the greatness that God has in store for our lives and from achieving what we were purposed for.

"Bravo," Hudson jumped to his feet applauding the youth. "Bravo." He stood in the middle of his huge library and applauded Jim. "Now, my son, comes the irresistible and final truth, or as the French say, the piece de resistance, where it all comes together. You mentioned it once already today, but before I focus you in on it, let me tell you a story. When I was younger man, I had taken my family up to our lake home. My daughter, son and I were down at the boathouse getting the boat ready for a ride. My daughter was seven and my boy was about three years old. The children were playing on the pier that ran alongside the boat house. I realized we were short a life vest and I asked my daughter to watch her brother while I went up to the house to get another. When I came out of house, my little girl was running toward me screaming, waving her hands.

"Daddy, Daddy, hurry!" she screamed. "Jeffy has fallen off the pier, hurrrrrry!"

"I sprinted toward the pier, ran out to the end and looked over the water in desperation. My son was nowhere in sight. I instinctively dove into the cold murky water and pushed toward the bottom. I frantically felt around the cold, muddy bottom, feeling for anything that resembled my little boy. I pleaded with God for help, held my breath for as long as possible and came up gasping for air. Pulling as much air into my lungs as I could, again I plunged to the bottom. Despairing, I combed every inch of the silty bottom. I was out of air and came back up again and sucked the air into my lungs. Just as I was about to dive down again, I saw two little hands wrapped around the pylon supporting the pier. I swam quickly around the backside only to find my precious son, cold, scared and holding on. I was stunned and asked, 'where were you?' And in an honesty only children know, he answered, 'I was here, Daddy, holding on until you could save me.'

"Success is just like that, Jim. You have to hold on until God purposes you with the success He has created for you. So when you add it all together, focusing on what you want, living in gratitude, doing all you can do, and realizing that all things are possible in God's timing, you are ready for the ultimate secret:

Trusting in God is nothing more than being pleasing to God. Pleasing God is nothing more than trusting Him. So trust by pleasing God and please by trusting God.

So the last key to wealth is: <u>seek to be pleasing to God in all things</u>.

Just as an apple tree will not produce oranges, you will only produce "good" things if you seek to be pleasing to God in all things.

Please always remember Jim who you are is God's gift to you; who you *choose* to become is your gift to God...so seek to please in all things.

Without this understanding, monetary wealth is somewhat like having a photograph of wealth, an image of the "real thing." Being truly wealthy is nothing more than living in the spirit of gratitude with a pleasing heart to serve God and others. Our friend David Hoffman is an excellent example of this."

"And so, Jim, I am confident this will make more sense as you grow older and gain more life experience; but in the meantime, I am proud of you and all you have learned. What I am most proud of is that you have accepted God's gift and pleased Him immensely by becoming one of his beloved children. Now, I speak this blessing over you: May God bless you bountifully and heap blessing upon you indeed, may He expand your capacity to be pleasing, may He keep his hand on you and show you great favor, and may he keep you from doubt and deception in every form so that no harm can befall you."

The Legacy of Wealth

"It Takes One Generation To Make Another"

Jon Bender

At 65, Jim had become the president and CEO of JCI Transnational holding company, which now controls interests in 7 companies worldwide and whose combined revenues exceed 10 billion dollars.

Jim focused with great attention as he pruned his prize rose bushes. He studied each branch and admired the tender stalk of the flower. The sound of young children laughing and playing filled the air, causing Jim to stop and smile. He was drawn to the laughter and stopped to look out over the carved granite railing that enclosed the terrace of his favorite rose garden. Birthday party preparations were in progress below. He was almost finished with his roses and would be joining the party momentarily; but, as he looked down, he absorbed the sight of his grandchildren scampering about, in and around the adults preparing for the party. He marveled at how quickly time had passed from his own sixth birthday many years ago to this present moment when he would help celebrate his son's 45th birthday.

Gratitude warmed his heart as he watched his family. His eyes briefly scanned the back of his huge estate which he had bought over two decades ago from Mr. Hudson. His mind wandered as his eyes were drawn up the granite walls to stained glass windows that illuminated the library. He remembered and smiled when he thought about how his life had been so radically transformed with what Hudson had shared with him in that room over forty years ago. He couldn't help but reflect with strong sentiment how he had been lifted up and challenged to become a man that would indeed be pleasing to God.

Jim's thoughts were interrupted by the cell phone tucked in his jacket pocket.

"Hello," Jim answered. "Hey Bob, what's the good news?"

"Just a quick update," Jim's legal advisor said. "I thought you would want to know that Carter has signed the merger documents.

Now it just needs to get the board's approval and we are golden …
and uh, well, there is one more thing."

"What's that?" Jim asked.

"Well, we have received twenty-one letters via FedEx over the
last two months, all addressed to you. All say the same thing, they're
from someone who wants to meet with you. We have sent them a
'Cease and Desist' order, we have tried to warn them, but now it's
gotten to the point of clear-cut harassment."

"Hmmm," Jim said pensively rubbing his chin.

"But there is one thing," Bob said. "It's a kid, he's sixteen years
old."

Jim grinned and then broke into a small chuckle. "You know
Bob, sometimes I think you guys are too smart for your own good.
Clearly the kid wants to meet with me about something. Wouldn't
the letters stop if you just set up the meeting?"

When the call was over, he slipped his cell phone back into
his pocket, turned and placed his hands on the granite railing and
laughed with a grateful heart as he looked out over his family below,
flipping his tarnished old silver dollar in his finger tips, reminiscing
about a certain 'ad' he had placed in the paper forty-nine years ago.

About The Author

Jon Bender has taught thousands of people in the area of generating wealth in both the corporate arena as well as home-based business. Jon is a top leader for the Direct Selling Association giant, EcoQuest International. He is the co-author of the premier wealth building system in the direct marketing industry, Creating Wealth From Home™.

Jon gives inspirational talks to thousands of people each year on purpose-driven wealth building principles. He specializes in teaching wealth building through proven systems, trust and gratitude.

As an Eagle Scout, Jon learned at a very young age about leadership and the importance of developing interpersonal skills. His quest for excellence in leadership launched his passion in the study of wealth building, personal growth and peak performance.

As a classically trained electrical engineer, systems specialist and co-author of four technology directories, Jon brings a fresh approach to value-centered and purpose-driven personal growth.

Prior to EcoQuest, Jon served as the Vice President of Business development for a division of the legendary personal growth publisher, Nightingale-Conant Corporation.

Jon is a devout Christian and lives with his wonderful wife Sherie and two young boys Nicholas and Alex in North Carolina.

Made in the USA
Lexington, KY
28 January 2015